ENID BLYTON'S

NATURE LOVER'S BOOK NUMBER 4

Animal and Nature Tales

First published in the U.K. in 1944 by
Evans Brothers Limited.
This edition was first published in 1971 by
Wm. Collins Sons & Co. Ltd.,
14 St. James's Place, London S.W.1.

Printed in Great Britain by
Love & Malcomson Ltd.,
Brighton Road, Redhill, Surrey.

NATURE LOVER'S BOOK

NUMBER 4

Animal and Nature Tales

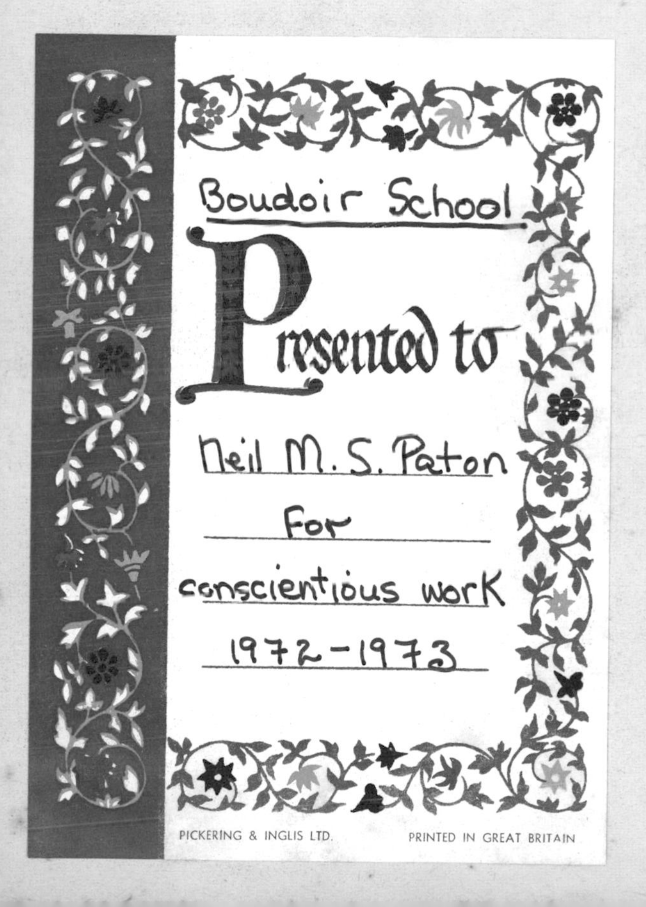

Other titles by Enid Blyton in Armada

Nature Lover's Book Number 1
Nature Lover's Book Number 2
Nature Lover's Book Number 3
The Naughtiest Girl in the School
The Adventurous Four
The Adventurous Four Again
The Island of Adventure
The Castle of Adventure
The Valley of Adventure
The Sea of Adventure
The Mountain of Adventure
The Ship of Adventure
The River of Adventure
The Circus of Adventure
The Rockingdown Mystery
The Rubadub Mystery
The Ring O'Bells Mystery
The Rilloby Fair Mystery
The Secret Island
The Secret of Killimooin
The Secret Mountain
The Secret of Spiggy Holes
The Secret of Moon Castle
Adventures on Willow Farm
Happy Day Stories
Rainy Day Stories
The Children at Green Meadows
The Put-Em-Rights
Six Cousins at Mistletoe Farm
Six Cousins Again
Those Dreadful Children
The Family at Red-Roofs
Hollow Tree House
House-at-the-Corner
Holiday House

THE SCHOOL SNOWMAN

It had snowed hard that morning, and the school playground was full of white, soft snow. "Let's come early this afternoon and build a snowman before school!" cried the children. "It will be such fun!"

So that afternoon they built a fine snowman. You should have seen him! They had made him a big tall body and a big round head. They had shaped arms for him and made round hands. Really, he looked fine!

"We must dress him!" cried Ronald. "I've got my daddy's old bowler hat. He shall wear it on his head!"

"And I've brought an old coat I found in the ditch this morning!" said Alan. "He will look fine in it, and I don't expect he will mind the holes a bit!"

"I've got a ragged pair of gloves for his funny white hands," said Amy.

"And I'll cut him a stick from the hedge!" said George.

They made him eyes with black stones, and a fine nose and mouth. They made him hair of straw, and they put the old black bowler hat on his head. They dressed him in the ragged coat, and they put the gloves on his cold hands. George cut him a stick from the hedge. Then they danced round him and yelled loudly.

The school bell rang, and they all trooped into their classroom, sometimes peeping out of the window during lessons to see the old snowman standing in the playground.

Now that night, whilst the old snowman was standing alone in the snow, two burglars came to take the money that Miss Brown always put away in her desk for the children's savings-bank. They broke a window at the back of the school and climbed through, though one of the men cut himself badly on the glass. They forced open Miss Brown's locked desk and took the money-box there.

"We'll open the school door and go out that way," said one man. "I don't want to cut myself again. Come on!"

So they slipped out of the school door into the playground—and there, in the darkness, they dimly saw the snowman, standing up straight and tall, as if he were watching for them.

"It's the policeman!" whispered one man to the other. "He's standing out there waiting to catch us! I can see his black helmet! What shall we do?"

"Go out the other way!" said the second man, in a fright. "Quick! Come on! I daren't go past that policeman!"

So they ran to the back of the school, and opened the broken window to climb out—and they fell straight into the arms of the real policeman who had come along and found the broken window! He was waiting there for them, thinking they would be sure to go back that way.

"What have you got in your pockets?" said the policeman sternly, and they had to show him the stolen money. So off they went to the police-station, very sorry for themselves.

And when the children heard next day that their old snowman had saved their pennies for them, they *were* proud of him! In fact, they have patted him so hard on the back that he is almost falling to pieces!

SNOW

Nothing is so quiet as the snow;
It falls from out a leaden sky
Upon the wintry ground to lie
Without a murmur, silently and slow.

Like a fleecy blanket, softly spread
Upon each sleeping field and hill,
It shelters them in warmth until
They stir and rouse within their wintry bed.

Then silent as it came, the dazzling snow
As silent goes, within a night;
And here and there the snowdrops white
Put up their heads, and sweetly nod and blow.

RIDDLE-ME-REE

My first is in Christmas, but not in December,
My second's in Guy Fawkes, but not in November,
My third is in pen, but isn't in ink,
My fourth is in peony, pansy and pink,
My fifth is in yellow, but isn't in blue,
My sixth is in doing, but never in do,
My seventh's in eagle, but not in its wing,
My eighth is in wedding, but isn't in ring,
My ninth is in many, but never in more,
My tenth is in apple, and also in core,
My eleventh's in Ada and Alice and Ann,
My twelfth is in riddle, now guess if you can!
My whole is a greeting we send every year,
Just let me whisper it into your ear!
(Answer: Happy New Year!)

THE BLACKBIRD IS SINGING

HERE'S the New Year—now what will it bring?
Apples in autumn, bluebells in spring,
Pussy-palm soft as a grey kitten's fur,
Poppies a-dancing when summer winds stir,
Yellow-clad fields where the buttercups gleam,
New little ducks on the chattering stream,
Eggs in the hedgerows, lambs skipping by,
Woods full of primroses, little and shy.
Yellow bees droning in summery heat,
Early nuts ripening, blackberries sweet;
All these and more the New Year is bringing—
Really, no wonder the blackbird is singing!

STONES FOR A HORSE

TOM was very cross. His father had told him to fetch Bess, the old horse, from the field on the hill and take her to Farmer Brown's, who wanted to borrow her for a day's work.

"It's Saturday," he grumbled. "I've been at school all the week, Dad—can't I have a day off for once? I told Billy Jones we'd take our dinner and walk over to the next village to see the football match."

"You'll do as you're told, my boy, without any fuss!" said his father sternly. "If you go now, and bring Bess back at once, you will have plenty of time to call for Billy and walk over to the match."

It was a cold day and the roads were like ice. Tom sulkily put on his thick coat and started off. Bother Bess!

He walked down the slippery hill, and then cut across the fields up the opposite hill towards the big field where Bess stood, waiting to be fetched to work. She was a big and gentle old horse, but she was not very fond of Tom, who was a rough and impatient boy.

"Come on, now!" shouted Tom, holding open the gate for Bess. "Hurry yourself! You're going to Farmer Brown's!"

Bess understood. She lumbered out of the gate at a canter, and Tom gave her a cut with his switch as she passed. Down the fields she went, keeping well in front of Tom and his switch, and then turned into the lane to go up the hill to the farm.

But that hill was like an ice-slide! Bess dug her hoofs into the road, but she found herself slipping all over the place. She found it very difficult to prevent herself from falling down.

Tom was angry. "Get on there, get on!" he shouted from some distance behind. But Bess couldn't get on, no matter how she tried. Then Tom lost his temper. He picked up a handful of stones and threw them at Bess. They clattered all round her and frightened her terribly. She struggled again and nearly fell over. She could *not* get up that icy hill. Tom was in a real rage now and threw more and more stones at the horse. He was afraid that he would be too late to go to the football match.

Then someone shouted to him: "Hie, what do you think you're doing with those stones?" Tom turned. It was Billy Jones, come to look for him to go to the match.

"Can't you see!" yelled Tom. "I'm throwing them at this silly horse to make her go up the hill."

"That's the wrong way to use stones," said Billy at once. "Look here!"

He ran to the laneside and picked up handfuls of pebbles. Then he went over to the struggling horse and spoke gently to her, and scattered pebbles under her feet. Back he went and got more stones. Soon Bess was able to tread the road safely, for the stones helped her to grip the road.

"Use stones if you like, but not for *throwing*!" said Billy. Tom didn't say anything, but I expect he felt ashamed of himself, don't you?

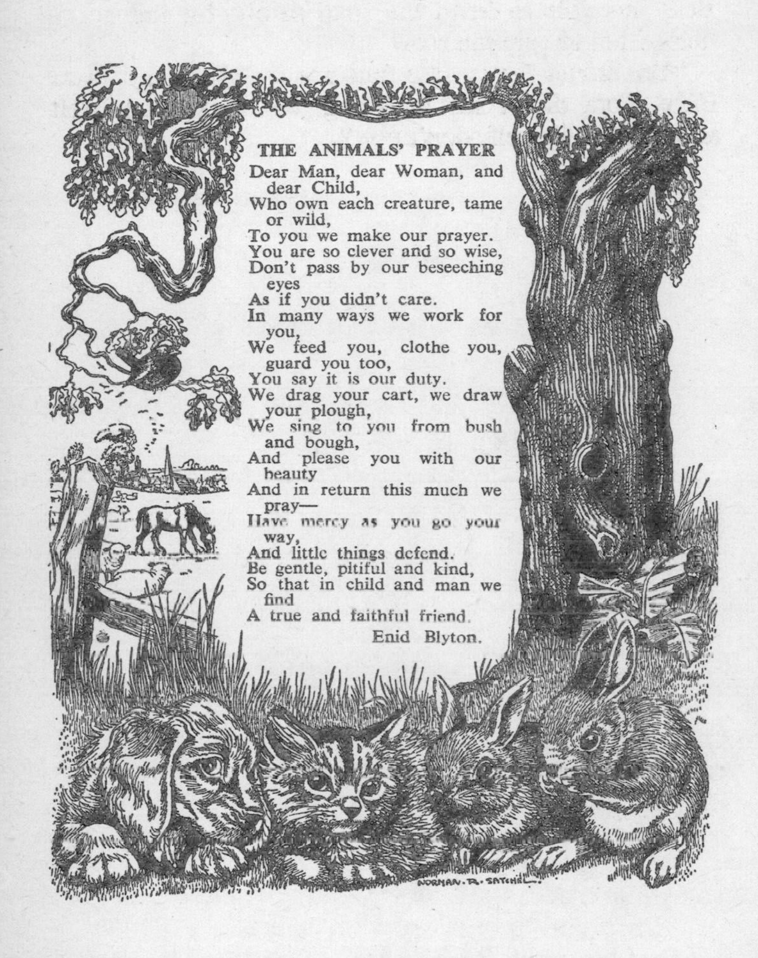

THE ANIMALS' PRAYER

Dear Man, dear Woman, and dear Child,
Who own each creature, tame or wild,
To you we make our prayer.
You are so clever and so wise,
Don't pass by our beseeching eyes
As if you didn't care.
In many ways we work for you,
We feed you, clothe you, guard you too,
You say it is our duty.
We drag your cart, we draw your plough,
We sing to you from bush and bough,
And please you with our beauty
And in return this much we pray—
Have mercy as you go your way,
And little things defend.
Be gentle, pitiful and kind,
So that in child and man we find
A true and faithful friend.

Enid Blyton.

ON THE BIRD-TABLE

THE robin is there with his bold black eye,
And the hedge-sparrow brown,
The chaffinch hops, so merry and spry,
And the thrush flies down.
The starlings jostle each other, and gobble
The fat off the plate,
The sparrows chatter and feast and squabble,
The blackbirds wait.
The tits hang light on the pea-nut string,
Upside down,
The wren arrives on his whirring wing,
Stumpy and brown.

Feast little birds, and eat your fill
The whole day long;
The payment, please, is a little trill,
Or a short sweet song!

NOW, BRER RABBIT!

ONE fine morning Brer Rabbit came along with an empty sack, looking for something good to put into it—and round the corner came old Brer Fox with a full one over his shoulder.

"Heyo, Brer Fox!" said Brer Rabbit. "What have you got in that sack?"

"Fish," said Brer Fox, with a grin. "Fish that I caught for *myself*, Brer Rabbit. Folks that are too lazy to go fishing don't get fish for dinner!"

"Let's have a look," said Brer Rabbit. He peeped in at the top of Brer Fox's sack, and didn't his mouth water when he saw the nice little fishes Brer Fox had got there!

"Your sack wouldn't be nearly so heavy to carry if you let me have a few of those fish," said Brer Rabbit.

"And your face would look better if you weren't so full of cheek!" said Brer Fox smartly. "Give me a hand up with my sack, Brer Rabbit—heave it up on to my shoulder again."

Brer Rabbit gave the sack a heave—and at the same time he gave the sack a little slit with his knife! A slippery fish popped out of the hole and Brer Rabbit took it in his hand.

"Well, good-bye, Brer Fox," he said, with a grin. "I'm going the same way as you—but I know you don't like my company, so I'll walk a good way behind you! Take care that heavy sack doesn't hurt your shoulder!"

"Huh, I don't even feel the weight of it!" said Brer Fox. "It feels as light as a feather to me!"

Off he went—and behind him a little way walked Brer Rabbit, twirling his whiskers and grinning as usual. Every so often he bent down and picked up something—for at every few steps a small fish slipped out of the hole in Brer Fox's sack to the ground. Brer Rabbit picked each one up and put it into his own sack. Brer Fox stepped along well, and as he went he sang a song he had made up himself:

"Hi yi, tingalees,
Brer Rabbit won't get any of these,
Hi yi, tingalees!"

Half-way home his sack began to feel lighter. Brer Fox was pleased. "Didn't I say I didn't even feel the weight of the sack!" he said to himself. "It's as light as a feather!"

It went on getting lighter as more and more fish slipped out—and Brer Rabbit's sack went on getting heavier. When Brer Fox arrived home *his* sack was empty—but the one on Brer Rabbit's back was full and brimming over! Brer Fox took his sack off his shoulder and looked at it in astonishment and dismay. Where were his fish?

He saw Brer Rabbit coming up with a full sack, and he yelled at him.

"Where did those fish come from?"

"Out of the brook, I guess," said Brer Rabbit, with a grin. "Would you like one, Brer Fox? You wouldn't give me one of yours just now—but I don't bear ill-will—you can have *two* of mine if you like!"

"Those are *my* fish!" yelled Brer Fox, in a fury.

"Oh, well, if they jumped from your sack into mine you can't blame them," said Brer Rabbit, edging away. "Maybe they didn't like your company, Brer Fox—and I don't wonder! I'm not very fond of it either!"

And off ran Brer Rabbit with the fish, and as he went he hummed a song:

"Hi yi, tingalees,
Brer Fox, he won't get any of these,
Hi yi, tingalees!"

TREES IN WINTER

ELM and chestnut and beech and lime
Are bare and brown in the winter-time,
Oak and sycamore, birch and plane,
Have hardly a leaf to catch the rain!
Ash and maple and poplar tall
Haven't a leaf to show at all!

But holly and fir and cedar and pine
Stand up straight in a well-dressed line,
And juniper, privet, laurel and yew
Wear their leaves all the winter through!
Maybe they feel the cold and so
They never undress when the chill winds
blow!

FIND THESE HIDDEN TREES

1. Will you peel me an orange?
2. A wasp and a bee chanced to meet in the honey.
3. Good-bye, Tom! A pleasant journey to you!
4. There is a mist or heat-haze lying over the hills.
5. At the Zoo a kangaroo boxed with its keeper.
6. Put a drop in each cup.
7. If I run I get out of breath.
8. You did not understand all I meant.
9. The hollyhock grew as high as the roof.

(*Answers:* Elm; Beech; Maple; Hazel; Oak; Pine; Fir; Lime; Ash.)

THE ELM-TREE AND THE WILLOW

SIDE by side in the hedge grew a great elm and a sapling willow. The willow was growing in the shade of the elm, and it did not get enough light or sunshine, but it did the best it could. It sent its thin roots down into the earth to look for water, and it put out long shoots to try to reach the sunshine.

The big elm scorned the small willow. It raised its head very high in the air, it grew thousands of small leaves, and in the wind it made such a rushing noise that it drowned the voice of the little willow.

The willow sometimes spoke timidly to the tall elm. It asked the great tree questions about the birds that nested every year in the bushy trunk of the elm. It admired the pretty red blossoms that grew on the big tree's twigs in the early spring, and which it flung down to the ground when the wind blew.

"Ah, you should grow blossoms like mine!" said the elm. "Look at your silly little green catkins! And, see—when the autumn comes I send thousands of winged fruits spinning through the air for the children to catch. They love me—I am tall and grand, my leaves shout in the wind, I give welcome shade in the hot summer—but you are a miserable little thing!"

"Well, I cannot grow very big because you take so much light and sunshine from me," said the willow humbly. "But, great elm-tree, I believe my roots go farther down than yours do."

"Pooh! What do roots matter!" said the elm-tree impatiently. "They don't show, do they?"

Now that autumn there came a great gale one dark, stormy night. The wind rushed through the trees, and the elm shouted so loudly that the willow was nearly deafened. The great tree swayed to and fro, and the willow bent, too. The wind grew wilder and wilder, and the elm shouted more and more loudly—and then suddenly a terrifying thing happened.

The great elm bent so far over that it could not get its trunk back straight again. Its poor, weak roots could not hold it, and they broke. The tree gave a loud moaning cry and toppled heavily to the ground.

The willow was left alone to bear the strong gusts of wind. It was frightened. If the elm had fallen, surely it, too, would fall, for it was but a small tree. The wind pulled hard at it, but the willow's roots were deep and held it well. When the storm at last died down, the willow was still standing—and by it lay the great elm, its leaves dying by the thousand.

The wind came by once more and whispered to the willow, "Roots don't show, but they matter most of all! Roots don't show, but they matter most of all!"

THE CAUTIOUS SNAIL

SAYS the curly snail, "I've a little front door,
And when winter is here it is shut,
But now that the sunshine is warm once more
I think I will open it,
BUT
I shan't go wandering near and far
With my little head out of my shell
Until, Mister Blackbird, I know where *you* are,
For if you set eyes on me,
WELL!
I know what will happen, for down you'll fly,
And close beside me you'll hop,
You'll hammer me hard on a stone nearby
And you won't hear me squealing out
STOP!
So I'm going to be cautious when opening my door,
I'll put out one eye to see;
You may have had snails by the hundred before,
But you won't make your dinner off
ME!"

THE LION AND THE MOUSE

Characters

THE LION.
THE MOUSE.
THE HUNTER.

(*The scene is in a wood. A mouse is running about looking for food.*)

MOUSE. I'm hungry to-day! I wish I could find something to eat! Ah, here is a nice juicy stalk! (*Nibbles it.*) The big lion was about yesterday and I was too afraid to come out of my hole to eat. I don't expect he would have noticed a little mouse—but he might have, and then that would be the end of me!

(*Roaring heard off stage.*)

MOUSE. Oh, tails and whiskers! Oh, cheese and biscuits! That's the lion again! Whatever shall I do? I'm far away from my hole, and I can't see any safe place here! (*Runs about distractedly.*)

(*Roaring heard again.*)

MOUSE (*squeaking*). Oh! Oh! There he is again! Where can I hide? Where can I hide? Will the lion see me if I hide behind this log? (*Runs there and crouches down. Enter* LION, *roaring.*)

LION. I'm hungry! I've had nothing to eat for ages! I could even eat blackbeetles! (*Stands and sniffs.*)

LION. I smell something! I smell—MOUSE! Yes—MOUSE!

(*Goes sniffing all round—and comes to the* MOUSE. *Puts out paw quickly and drags* MOUSE *to front.*)

LION. Ha! I thought I smelt mouse! Now I've got you—but I wish you were fatter!

MOUSE. Spare me, spare me, great big lion! I'm so small and you are so big. Be merciful, great big lion! Be merciful!

LION. Not I! I'm hungry, I tell you!

MOUSE. Lion, have mercy on a little creature like me! I have never done any harm. I run about and enjoy my little life. Let me go, I pray you, great big lion!

LION. No. I'm hungry and I'd like to eat you.

MOUSE. But I'd only be a mouthful! Lion, let me go, and there may come a time when I can repay you for your mercy and kindness.

LION (*roaring with laughter*). Ha ha, ho ho! That's a funny joke! Who ever heard of a tiny mouse helping a great big lion! No, no, mouse—that could never happen. I should never need your help.

MOUSE. Let me go, lion—and I promise you that one day I will return your kindness if I can!

LION (*taking away his paw*). Very well. I *will* let you go—though I am quite sure you will never be able to help *me*!

MOUSE (*running off.*) Oh, thank you, thank you, great big lion. I am very grateful to you. (*Goes out.*)

LION. Well—it's good to be merciful and kind—but I am still very hungry! I am sleepy too. I will lie down and have a rest whilst the sun is hot.

(*Lies down and falls asleep. There is a sound of somebody whistling off stage. Enter the* HUNTER, *carrying a gun and a net. He stops at sight of* LION, *and is most surprised.*)

HUNTER. Ha! a lion! I've been hunting him all morning—and now I find him here, fast asleep! I can take him all alive-oh! Now—where's my net? (*Unfolds netting, creeps towards* LION.)

HUNTER. I'll throw this strong net all around the lion

—and then when he awakes he will be caught. He will struggle—and he will get himself more and more tangled in my net!

(*Throws net over sleeping* LION. *The* LION *awakes with a roar. Springs up, and finds himself caught in net. Begins to struggle and gets himself more entangled. Rolls over and over on ground, roaring.*)

HUNTER. Roar away, lion! You are well caught! That net is strong and you will not be able to get free of it! I shall go to fetch my companions—and then we will take you alive!

(*Goes out.*)

LION. Help! Help! I'm caught! This net is holding me! Help, help! (*Rolls over again, etc.*) Oh, what shall I do? The hunter will soon be back with his friends and I shall be their prisoner! If only I could bite this net to pieces—but the more I struggle, the tighter it holds me!

(*Struggles again. Enter the* MOUSE—*stops in surprise to see the* LION *in net.*)

MOUSE (*squeaking*). Oh! Oh! You are caught, great lion! Can't you get free?

LION (*with a roar*). No! This net holds me everywhere! Ah, little mouse, if only you could do me a good turn! Now is your chance—but alas, you are so little that you cannot possibly help a great animal like me!

MOUSE. Ah, lion, that is where you are wrong! I *can* help you! I can set you free!

LION. Nonsense, little mouse! How can you set me free if I with my great strength cannot set myself free?

MOUSE. With my sharp little teeth I can nibble the net—like this—and this—and this! See how I have bitten the string through, lion! You see, my teeth are made for nibbling!

LION. Little mouse, I believe you *can* help me! Quick! Use your sharp little teeth well, and perhaps you will free me before the hunter returns!

MOUSE. I will nibble—and nibble—and nibble! Lie still, great big lion, and let me nibble as fast as I can!

LION. Hurry then! Ah, this paw is free now! Good. And now this one is free—you work quickly, little mouse.

MOUSE. I have nibbled—and nibbled—and nibbled! Shake your head, lion, and maybe the net will fall away from you, for I have nibbled away the knots!

(LION *shakes himself—the net falls off—he jumps to his feet, steps out of the net, and is free.*)

LION. Thank you, tiny mouse! You have saved my life! I didn't think, when I let you go from under my paw a little while ago, that you would ever be able to help *me* in return! But you have, and I am grateful. Thank you, little mouse!

MOUSE. Little things can often help big things, Sir Lion—and a little mercy and kindness are never wasted! Good-bye! Run whilst you can—you are quite safe now!

(MOUSE *runs one way.* LION *goes the other.*)

CURTAIN

MARCH COMES IN

FEBRUARY slips from the garden cold,
  Bidding the snowdrops good-bye,
The crocuses shine in their purple and gold
  And the aconites stare at the sky.

"Farewell!" says February—then she is flown,
  And the garden falls silent and still;
A violet is peeping there, shy, all alone,
  And a robin hops up with a trill.

They are waiting for March—and longing to see
  If he'll come like a lamb, soft and light,
Or rage like a lion, as loud as can be,
  Making the trees shake in fright.

The garden is watching and waiting—it knows
If he comes like a lamb, like a lion he goes!

A PUZZLE

THE HERALD

HE stood beside the little pond,
His golden trumpet showing;
Spring was dancing just beyond,
Where primroses were growing.
She tiptoed near; the herald blew
A fanfare, gay and shrill;
Spring knew the herald—so do you!
The golden . . . . !

(*What flower has a trumpet to blow? The daffodil!*)

PINK-PINK

(*The chaffinch is calling "pink-pink" now in our gardens.*)

"PINKITY-PINK!" the chaffinch cried,
And he cocked his neat little head on one side.

"What is pink, you dear little fellow?
The dancing daffies are all of them yellow!"

He scattered the bloom of the big almond tree,
"It's pink-pink-pink!" he said. "Pink! Can't you see?"

"And the buds on the hawthorn—how rosy they grow!
Pink-pink-pink, in the long hedgerow!

"The daisies, too, in the grass by your feet,
They're all tipped with pink! Pink-pink, they are sweet!"

Then off he flew gaily, and all the day through
I hear him call "Pinkity-pink!" Do *you*?"

BRER BEAR'S BAND

ONCE upon a time Brer Bear got up a band. He was very fond of music, and he had an idea he could play the drum well. So he spoke to Brer Wolf, Brer Fox, Brer Possum and Brer Turkey Buzzard, and said how fine it would be if they could get up a band and play for parties and dances.

"We won't ask that sly Brer Rabbit," said Brer Fox, when he heard all Brer Bear had to say. "Leave him out. We've enough without him. He won't like being left out of it—serve him right!"

Well, the band very soon began. Brer Wolf played the saxophone. Brer Fox played the fiddle. Brer Possum performed on the piano. Brer Bear banged the drums, and Brer Turkey Buzzard sang to the music because he had a very loud voice. It needed a loud voice to be heard above Brer Bear's drumming. Brer Bear didn't bother much about keeping time with the others—he just enjoyed himself with the drumsticks.

Brer Rabbit was surprised that he was left out. He listened to the others practising and grinned to himself. He heard Brer Bear banging away at the drum, and he heard Brer Turkey Buzzard screeching away trying to make himself heard. He peeped in at the window and saw, at the back of the room, a small table on which was a nice little supper laid ready for the band when they had finished practising. Brer Rabbit liked the look of that supper—chicken and salad and an ice-cream pudding. He really did feel sorry that he didn't belong to the band when he saw that supper.

Brer Rabbit went and banged at the door when the band finished the piece they were playing. Brer Bear opened it. Brer Rabbit seemed to be surprised when he saw Brer Bear with drumsticks.

"Are you going to practise with your band to-night?" he asked.

"We *have* been!" said Brer Bear indignantly. "You must have heard us when you were coming along!"

"Funny!" said Brer Rabbit. "Couldn't hear a note! Maybe you play too softly."

"Boys, play up again and let Brer Rabbit hear how we sound!" roared Brer Bear. "Go outside and listen, Brer Rabbit." So Brer Rabbit went outside—but he put his paws into his ears, and didn't hear a thing, though the band played like a thunder-storm.

"Sorry, Brer Bear," said Brer Rabbit, putting his head indoors. "Couldn't hear a thing! You come on out here and listen, all of you. You won't hear a note either. It's a pity to have a band that can't be heard a few yards away!"

All the bandsmen put down their instruments and went outside to listen. Brer Rabbit slipped inside and shut the door. The bandsmen listened hard.

"It's true," said Brer Bear. "I can't hear a note!"

"It's queer," said Brer Possum. "You bang that drum so hard, too, Brer Bear."

"Can't even hear the saxophone," said Brer Turkey Buzzard. "I say, boys—let's go in and ask Brer Rabbit to be our conductor. Maybe he could tell us how to make a bit more noise."

So they all trooped in to ask Brer Rabbit—but Brer Rabbit was gone! So was the supper! Not even a scraping of ice-pudding was left!

Brer Rabbit laughed till he ached that night—but the bandsmen never knew how it was they couldn't hear their band playing from outside! Do *you* know?

A COUNTY PUZZLE FOR YOU

(*You may like to use an atlas for this puzzle. In each of the sentences there is part of the name of a British county.*)

1. The cock crowed loudly on the *wall*.
2. This is my *cash*-box, I had it for Christmas.
3. When I dropped the glass it *broke* into twenty pieces.
4. The bicycle wheel got into a *rut* and Jim fell off.
5. The cow chews the *cud* each day.
6. I am so tired that I think I shall go to *bed*.
7. This steak *fries* quickly.
8. Open your *mouth* as wide as you can.

(*Answers:* Cornwall; Lancashire; Pembrokeshire; Rutland; Kirkcudbrightshire; Bedfordshire; Dumfriesshire; Monmouthshire.)

THE FIRST LAMB

Down at the farm in a warm sheltered place
Is the first little lamb of the spring,
It looks all around with its funny black face,
Such a tiny, unsteady wee thing!
Its voice is so small, it is hardly a bleat,
"Maa-aa!" it cries, all the day,
It springs here and there on its four little feet,
And begs its big mother to play!
It wriggles its tail like the catkins that grow
In the sheltering hedges behind,
It leaps and it dances on tippity-toe,
While the mother-sheep, sleepy and kind,
Blinks at her lamb, and wonders to see
Such a hoppetty, skippetty mite,
No wonder the children, as pleased as can be,
Come peeping at such a sweet sight!

THE FUNNY DREAM

Once upon a time there was a little girl called Elsa, who went to school and did lessons just as you do. Twice a week there was Nature Lesson—and, you know, Elsa was really very bad at this. She was the only child who never brought a flower, a twig, or even a leaf. She just didn't bother.

One day her teacher said, "Now on Thursday I think it would be nice to have a look at some hazel catkins. They are such pretty things. We will put them in water and watch them get fluffy and powdery. Who will bring some? Will *you*, Elsa?"

"I don't know where there are any, Miss Brown,"

Elsa said—and she thought, "I'm not going to bother to look, either!"

Now that night Elsa had a very peculiar dream. She dreamt that she was going down the road to school and she met a tiny little man carrying an enormous pair of scissors.

"Can you tell me where there are any lambs?" he asked Elsa.

"Yes," said Elsa. "There are some in the field on the hill over there. Why do you want to know?"

"Oh, I want to cut off their tails and make some soup with them," said the little man, and he showed her his big scissors.

"What a horrid, unkind thing to do!" said Elsa, shocked. "The farmer will be after you if you do that!"

"He won't know!" said the little man, and ran off to the hillside where the lambs were playing. Elsa ran after him, quite determined to stop him cutting off the tails of the little lambs. But he sped on so fast that she couldn't catch him up. So she made up her mind to go to the farmhouse and tell the farmer.

The farmer was most surprised to hear her tale. He clapped his hat on his head and strode off with Elsa beside him.

"There's the little man!" said Elsa, pointing to the other side of the field. "Oh, look! He's got a sack—and it's full! We are too late!"

"I'll give him such a spanking!" roared the farmer, and he raced across the field—but the little man saw him coming, and, quick as lightning, he opened his sack, shook out all the little fluffy tails he had there, and let them fly on the breeze. They blew into the hedge—and when the farmer got to him and took his sack away it was quite empty! The little man grinned wickedly and said, "I've thrown them away—but I'll come and find them to-morrow!" He ran off and disappeared.

Elsa looked at the hedge—and there, growing on the hazel twigs, were all the little lambs' tails shaking in the wind! She was just going to point them out to the farmer when she awoke. She was in bed—and had been dreaming.

"It was a very funny dream," said Elsa. "I really think I must go to that hedge on the hillside to-morrow and see if those lambs' tails are there!"

So she trotted off before school the next morning—and, sure enough, the hedge was covered with hazel catkins—little lambs' tails blowing in the wind! Elsa picked some and ran to school.

"Why, how lovely, Elsa!" said Miss Brown. "How did you know where to find them?"

"A wicked little man put them on the hedge," said Elsa. "He said he was going to get them to-day—but I got them first. They are *real* lambs' tails, Miss Brown!"

POCKETS

THE jumping kangaroo
Has a pocket made of skin.
It says, "Now this will do
To keep my baby in!"

The little humming bees
Buzz cheerfully and say,
"We've pockets in our knees
To carry goods away!"

"*I* have a pocket, too!"
The bat squeaks in surprise,
"I use it all night through
For beetles and for flies!"

Now, children, put your fist
Inside your pockets deep,
And write down in a list
The funny things *you* keep!

A PUZZLE

TAKE half a stag, the middle of a dog, the tail of a bear, the head of a cat, the middle of a gorilla and the tail of a fish. Then sort them out nicely and make me a big bird! Anyone clever enough?

(*Answer:* Ostrich)

FRIENDS

When in the woods I go
The squirrel does not frisk away,
The sandy rabbits come to play,
I am their friend, they know.

The hedgehog shuffles by,
The robin gives a creamy trill,
And all the little mice sit still
And stare with beady eye

They have no fear of me;
The toad peeps from his sheltering stone,
The fox comes trotting by alone;
I am their friend, you see!

SPRING FOLK

It was a warm spring day. Rain had fallen in the night, and everywhere was moist and soft. Prickles, the hedgehog, was hungry, for he had not long awakened from his winter sleep. A few slugs and perhaps half a dozen beetles would make a very nice dinner.

He left his hole in the bank of a ditch and shuffled through the dead leaves that still lay at the bottom. As he went he saw two bright brown eyes peeping at him from the bank above. It was the dormouse.

"Hallo, Dozy!" said the hedgehog. "I haven't seen you for a long while."

"I've been asleep," said the furry dormouse. "I had a hole near yours, but you didn't know it! Now I am awake, and I want to get fat and sleek! I am hunting for some dinner. I shall go to the farm for a few grains of corn."

"Beetles for me," said the hedgehog, and he ambled off again, his little piggy snout sniffing everywhere. He saw a long, slender snake gliding away as he came out of the ditch, and he called to the beautifully patterned creature.

"Slinky! Where have you been?"

The snake slid round and stared at the hedgehog. "I was asleep in an old willow," he said. "But the sun is warm now and I awoke. I am looking for a frog or two. I am very hungry."

"There are plenty in the pond," said the hedgehog. "Go and look. You can swim, I know."

The snake glided away to the pond. The hedgehog hurried on, looking for slugs. He came to the old mossy stone and looked underneath. There was a large toad there, blinking quietly to himself.

"So you're awake!" said the hedgehog. "I thought you'd be in the pond with the others."

"I *have* been there," said the toad. "Now I am here again for a rest. Those frogs are so noisy. I wish the flies would hurry up and come along. I am very hungry after my long winter sleep."

"The bees are awake, too," said the hedgehog. "I saw some just now. I don't think the queen wasp is about yet, though. I looked behind the thick ivy where she has hidden all winter, and she was still there."

"The lizards are back again. Look!" said the toad. The hedgehog looked up to the warm, sandy bank above him. Six small lizards played there, flicking their little bodies about quickly in the sunshine. The hedgehog shuffled up to speak to them.

They were off like a flash into their holes. They were not sleepy any more! But they were thin and hungry, and had been watching eagerly for any fly to come near them.

"Everyone is awake and hungry now," said the hedgehog to himself. "Good gracious me, whatever's that?"

He hurried to the old toad's stone and crouched down behind it. The toad cowered down lower. There was suddenly a great noise of chattering and laughing.

"It's the children coming out of school!" croaked the old toad. "I don't think they'll hurt us."

"How do *you* know?" said the hedgehog fearfully. "Maybe they have been asleep all winter, like us, and are thin and hungry, too! If they see us they may eat us for their dinner!"

But they needn't have been afraid, need they?

THE HAPPY HEDGEHOG

ALL through the winter the hedgehog slept sound,
And then he woke up and he took a walk round.
"Why, spring-time is here!" said the hedgehog, delighted.
"Winter has vanished—I do feel excited!"

He hurried along in the ditch wet with dew,
Meeting the mice and the voles that he knew.
But his friend, the old toad, had gone crawling away
To swim with the frogs in the pond all the day.

The hedgehog was starved and decidedly thinner,
"It's quite twenty weeks," he said, "since I had dinner."
So he ate seven ear-wigs, five beetles, one snail,
And a worm that he pulled from its hole by the tail.

The sun on his back made him beautifully hot,
He curled himself up in a wind-sheltered spot.
Said he, "I fear nobody, no one at all,
When I roll myself up in a prickly ball!"
So there he lies now, and if you should find him,
Set down a saucer of milk just behind him!
If only he'll stay in your garden, you'll see
What a very great help a small hedgehog can be!

A PUZZLE FOR YOU

In the following paragraph all the missing words are made up of four letters, the three last ones always being the same. Only the first letter changes each time. Who can fit in the right words first?

The woman . . . . down the path with a monkey. She was an old . . . , rather . . . . ; she said the monkey was . . . . and loved a . . . . , but all the . . . . I did not play with it, because of its . . . .—it was called Snappy!

(*Answer:* Came; Dame; Lame; Tame; Game; Same; Name.)

SPEEDWELL

Like a little pool of blue
On the bank we shine,
With brilliant eyes we gaze at you
When the day is fine.
The blue of summer skies we hold
In our blossoms frail,
Like little jewels we unfold,
Fit for fairy-tale.
Germander is the name we bear,
You call us "Speedwell", too,
See, we're shining everywhere,
Dressed in vivid blue.

THE RUNAWAY RABBIT

Characters

THE DISCONTENTED RABBIT. MRS. GOOSE.
HIS MOTHER. MISS CAT.
BROTHERS AND SISTERS, IF DESIRED. MASTER DOG.
MR. HORSE.

(*This is a good play for out-of-doors. The scene opens in wood, field or common. If played indoors, have branches of trees about, and a green cloth for grass. The* RABBIT *is sitting on a bank, reading. Enter his* MOTHER.)

MOTHER RABBIT. You naughty boy! Reading again, when there's such a lot of work to be done! Put away your book and help your brothers and sisters.

RABBIT. I don't want to. It is so dull helping to dress them and feed them. They are so stupid!

MOTHER. And I suppose you think yourself so clever! Well, let me tell you this, you are just as stupid a rabbit as your little brothers and sisters! Now come along quickly, and help me to give them their dinner.

RABBIT. I'm too clever for this family! I hate living with a crowd of silly rabbits! Mother, I've a good mind to run away and find somebody clever to live with. They would be so pleased to have a smart fellow like me for a friend.

MOTHER (*crossly*). Indeed! Well, let me tell you, you are quite wrong! Now come along quickly. (*She goes out.*)

RABBIT. I *shall* run away! I shall go and find somebody else to live with. Ah—who is this coming? It's big Mister Horse, who always looks so very clever and can do such marvellous things!

(*Enter* MR. HORSE. *He gallops round stage and neighs two or three times.*)

RABBIT. Good morning, Mr. Horse.

MR. HORSE. Good morning! Why aren't you helping your mother?

RABBIT. Oh, I'm too clever to waste my time at home! I want to run away and live with somebody really smart. I suppose I couldn't live with *you,* Mr. Horse, and do all that you do?

MR. HORSE. Well, can you drag a heavy cart along?

RABBIT. Oh dear me, no. I shouldn't like that at all!

MR. HORSE. Can you carry a heavy man on your back for miles and miles?

RABBIT. Good gracious, no! I'd be broken in half!

MR. HORSE. And can you kick like this! (*Turns back to* RABBIT *and kicks him.*)

RABBIT. Oh! Oh! You've hurt me! You horrid, unkind creature! I don't want to live with you or be like you! Go away!

MR. HORSE. Ho, ho, ho! What a little silly you are! Look, here's old Mrs. Goose. Maybe you'd like to live with *her*!

(*Canters off, neighing loudly.*)

(*Enter* MRS. GOOSE, *waddling and cackling.*)

MRS. GOOSE. Cackle, cackle, cackle! Good morning, little rabbit.

RABBIT. Good morning! Mrs. Goose, would you like a nice, clever friend? I want to run away and live with somebody smart.

MRS. GOOSE. Do you really? Well, can you lay nice big eggs?

RABBIT. Well, no, I can't.

MRS. GOOSE. I didn't think you'd be clever enough to do that. Can you hiss like this? (*Hisses most alarmingly, right in the* RABBIT'S *face.*)

RABBIT (*starting back*). Oh no, I could never do that. Besides, it's rude.

MRS. GOOSE. Oh, *is* it? Well, can you flap your wings like this? (*Flaps wings at* RABBIT *and knocks him right over.*)

RABBIT (*crying*). Oh, you horrid, unkind goose! I don't want to live with *you*! You know I haven't any wings to flap.

MRS. GOOSE (*waddling off*). Silly little rabbit! No eggs! No cackle! No hiss! No wings! Pooh! (*Goes off cackling loudly as if laughing.*)

RABBIT. Horrid creature. I shan't choose *her* for a friend!

(*Enter* MISS CAT, *very softly. She gives a meow.*)

RABBIT. Hallo, Miss Cat! I didn't hear you coming.

MISS CAT. No. I always walk very softly, you see. Why aren't you at home helping your mother?

RABBIT (*sulkily*). Oh, I'm tired of my stupid family. I want to live with somebody clever for a change. Could I live with *you*, Miss Cat, do you think, and learn to do all you do?

MISS CAT. Well, can you meow like this?

RABBIT (*listening to* CAT'S *meow*). Oh dear no, I couldn't possibly make a noise like that. I don't think it's a very nice noise, either.

MISS CAT. Oh, *don't* you! Well, can you catch mice and birds by jumping at them—like this! (*She jumps suddenly at the* RABBIT *and almost knocks him over.*)

RABBIT. Don't! you frighten me! No, I'm sure I could never catch mice and birds. I only like green things to eat.

MISS CAT. What a baby you are! Well, can you put out your claws and scratch like this? (*She suddenly slashes at his paw and scratches him. The* RABBIT *catches up his paw and nurses it in pain.*)

RABBIT. Oh! Oh! You cruel creature! You've scratched me and made me bleed. I'll never, never live with you!

MISS CAT (*making a sort of laughing meow*). Well, I don't want a silly animal like you for a friend. Good-bye! Try Mr. Dog—*he* may like a rabbit for company!

(*She goes out, meowing.*)

RABBIT. Well, I *will* try Mr. Dog. He always looks kind and good. I wonder where he is? (*Looks to left and right. Suddenly sees him, off-stage.*)

RABBIT. Mr. Dog! Mr. Dog! I want to talk to you for a minute.

MR. DOG (*off*). Coming! (*He patters in and looks at the* RABBIT.) What's the matter? Isn't it your dinner-time?

RABBIT. Yes—but I don't want to go and help my mother feed all those silly brothers and sisters of mine. I'm going to run away, Mr. Dog, and live with somebody clever. Do you think you could teach me the things you do?

MR. DOG. Well, all the things I do are quite easy. First of all, you must bark loudly like this. (*Barks loudly right in* RABBIT'S *ear.* RABBIT *shrinks back.*)

RABBIT (*alarmed*). I'm sure I could never make a noise like that.

MR. DOG. Well, can you growl deep in your throat, like this?

(*He growls in a terrifying manner, showing his teeth.* RABBIT *is still more alarmed.*)

RABBIT. Oh, what a dreadful noise! I couldn't make it, I'm sure.

MR. DOG. And now you must learn a most important thing—how to bite. You do it like this. (*Snaps suddenly at* RABBIT *and bites him.* RABBIT *screams.*)

RABBIT. Don't! Don't! You've bitten me! You horrid thing, you've bitten me! Mother, Mother, where are you? Save me from this cruel dog!

(*Enter* MOTHER RABBIT, *running.*)

MOTHER. Is that dog attacking you? How dare you, how dare you! I'll kick you up in the sky with my strong hind-legs!

MR. DOG. Now, don't get upset, Mother Rabbit. I'm only trying to teach your little rabbit how to be a dog.

RABBIT (*sobbing*). I don't want to be a dog. I don't want to be a cat. I don't want to be a goose. I don't want to be a horse. I want to be a little rabbit, and live with my mother and brothers and sisters. Boo-hoo-hoo!

MOTHER. There, there! Don't cry any more, but come and have your dinner. Go away, Mr. Dog. I am sure you have taught this silly rabbit a good lesson, but I don't want you to frighten my other children! Good-bye!

MR. DOG. Good-bye, Mother Rabbit. Good-bye, silly baby rabbit!

(*Trots off barking loudly.*)

RABBIT. Oh, please forgive me, Mother, and let me go to our burrow with you and have dinner with the others. I won't ever be so silly again! I thought I was so clever—but now I know I'm not!

MOTHER. Well, come along then—and just be a good rabbit in future!

(*They go off as curtain falls.*)

GOOD ADVICE

THERE was a bird who didn't know
Where to build his nest—and so
He asked the other birds he knew
If they would tell him what to do.

"Build high up among the trees,"
Said the rook, "and then the breeze
Will rock your babies all the day!"
The owl said, "Why, they'll blow away!
Put your nest inside a hole
Deep within some big tree's bole."
The robin shook his perky head,
"A pot or kettle's best," he said,
"A broken saucepan or a tin—
They're all good spots for nesting in."
The sparrow chirped and said his say,
"You'd better build your nest of hay
And tuck it at the gutter's end."
The jackdaw said, "No, no, my friend,
Build it in a high church steeple,
Far away from prying people."
"Pooh!" the cuckoo cried, "it's best
Not to bother with a nest!"

"Thank you," said the little bird,
"Such good advice is seldom heard.
So many spots there are to use
I really don't know which to choose!"

A PUZZLE FOR YOU

I AM something that men and horses wear; alter my tail and you may put me in a gun; change my second letter and you will be sure to find me coming down your chimney; give me another head and you may slip my first on my last and go a-walking.

Find the words. (*Answer:* Shoe; Shot; Soot, Foot).

THE OLD BOOT

THERE was once an old boot. It lay in a ditch, burst open at the toes, worn down at the heel and with its laces missing. Once it had been a very grand boot—so grand that it had been worn by a Prince. Think of that! It had been proud then, with a servant to polish it up every day and to make it shine brilliantly. Its brother boot lived with it, and they talked together all day long, very happily.

Then the Prince had bought some new boots, and had given his old ones to his servant. The man was proud to have such grand boots and wore them every Sunday—but when they wanted mending he couldn't be bothered with them, and he told his wife to give them away at the door next time a pedlar came round with some plants. So the boots were given to a ragged old pedlar, and he gave the servant's wife a fine fern for them.

They did not fit the pedlar very well, especially one of them, for his right foot was much bigger than his left. They were never cleaned now, and never mended. They grew old and wrinkled, and one of them burst at the toes. The pedlar grumbled bitterly at the boots, and one day, when he found an old shoe by the roadside, he flung off one of the boots, put on the shoe instead, and threw the old boot into the ditch. Then, limping, he went off down the road, wearing one boot and one shoe.

Then the old boot in the ditch was lonely, for it no longer had its brother boot to talk with. Spiders ran over it. A beetle went inside it. The rain soaked it through and through, and some grass seeds took root inside and grew there. The boot was sad and ashamed to think what it had come to. No one cared anything for it now, lost and forgotten in a wayside ditch.

Then one day in spring a red-breasted robin flew down to the ditch and turned over some dead leaves there. He saw the old boot and perched on the side, peering this way and that. Then he uttered a little trill and called his wife to him.

"See! what a wonderful place for a nest! You know how we robins love to build in something that has belonged to man, our friend. Well, here is a splendid boot, just right for a nest! What a piece of luck!"

Then, to the great delight of the old boot, the robins built their nest there. How carefully they built it of grass-roots, fibres, moss and leaves! The boot marvelled at the way they used their beaks to weave such a cosy home. It liked to feel their tiny feet perching here and there, and loved to listen to their creamy voices when they sang.

Four red-brown eggs were laid in the old boot. How proud it was! And how much prouder when the eggs hatched out into tiny birds, which were soon covered with softest down and feathers. It listened contentedly to their chatter, and was excited when they first tried their tiny wings.

"Thank you, old boot!" sang the robins, when their youngsters had all flown. "You kept our family safe!"

The boot was lonely when the robins were gone—but an adventure was still to come to it. For one day two children found it, with the old robins' nest still inside.

"A find, a find!" they cried. "Let's take it to school, and put it in the museum there! Everyone will love to see it!"

They did, and now the old boot has the place of honour in the school museum and is as happy as can be. I know, because I've seen it there!

THE CUCKOO SPEAKS

WHERE'S a nest, where's a nest!
Cuckoo!
Hedge-sparrow's will be the best,
Here is one with eggs of blue,
Watch and see what I will do,
Cuckoo!

In the nest so neatly made,
Cuckoo!
My own egg is quickly laid,
Then I fly away—and see
Sparrow's egg I take with me,
Cuckoo!

In the nest my egg will stay,
Cuckoo!
Till it hatches out one day,
Then the nestling there will grow
And fling the others down below,
Cuckoo!

My baby birds I never see,
Cuckoo!
I make others work for me,
I'm a wicked bird, it's clear,
Yet you welcome me each year,
Cuckoo!

THE SURPRISING EASTER EGG

JOAN was going to a party. She was all ready. She had on her new pink silk frock, a ribbon round her hair, her shoes in a bag, and a clean handkerchief in her pocket. She felt so excited, for she loved parties almost better than anything else.

"Now it's time you started," said Mother. "Good-bye, Joan. Have a lovely time—and remember to say thank you very much to Mrs. Jones when you leave."

"I won't forget!" said Joan happily. She ran down the garden path and out into the lane. What fun it was to be going to a party! Little Ellen Jones' birthday fell in Easter week this year, and it was going to be a lovely party, with an Easter egg for everyone to take home. Joan felt very happy.

She skipped down the lane past Mrs. White's house. Joan always stopped and looked over the gate at Mrs. White's, because she had two lovely Persian cats—blue-grey, with great orange eyes and long thick fur. Joan loved all animals—and wasn't it a pity, she had no pet of her own at all! No dog, no cat, no goldfish even, lived at Joan's house. No one had thought of letting Joan have a pet. Joan's mother was not very fond of animals, so she didn't bother about them.

Joan looked over Mrs. White's gate, hoping to see one of the lovely Persian cats somewhere in the garden. They loved Joan and always came running to her to be stroked. Joan knew that they had six little kittens just now—and how she longed to see them! But Mrs. White was rather a grand sort of lady, and Joan didn't like to ask her if she might go and see the kittens.

There were no cats in the garden at all, so Joan went on her way down the lane, thinking of the party, and wondering if there would be red or yellow jelly, and which she would choose. Half-way down the lane she passed an old tumble-down barn—and as she went by it she heard a noise that made her stop in surprise.

It was the mewing of cats! Now what could they be mewing for in the barn? Joan stopped and looked round. She saw a curious sight! One of Mrs. White's Persian cats was coming slowly along under the hedge—and in its mouth it carried one of its kittens! It was holding the kitten by the skin of its neck, as cats do. Joan was so surprised. She watched the cat slip under the hedge, make its way through the wet field, and disappear into the old barn.

The mewing still went on. Joan couldn't understand it. "Mrs. White's cat must have taken all her kittens into the barn!" she thought. "What a dreadful place to take them—so damp and cold and dirty! Poor little things!"

Joan found a hole in the hedge and squeezed through it. She went to the barn and peeped in. It was dark at first and she could hardly see anything. Then she discovered where the kittens were.

The mother-cat had climbed up a plank, and had put all her six kittens, one by one, on a shelf in the barn. There was a hole in the barn wall just there, and the wind came in. The kittens were cold and frightened. One crawled about the shelf—and then, to Joan's horror, it fell over the edge, bounced on the plank, and rolled to the ground!

It didn't seem to be hurt, but Joan was worried. Suppose they all fell off? Silly mother-cat, to put her kittens there!

"Oh dear, I shall be late for the party," thought Joan, "and I've got my best frock on. Whatever am I to do? I simply can't leave those kittens there."

She looked round for a ladder. There was an old one at the end of the barn. Joan dragged it across and put it up against the wall. She went up it and reached the shelf where the kittens were. There were five there —and one on the floor. The mother-cat was there too, and she purred when she saw Joan. Joan took hold of a kitten and carried it down the ladder. Then up she went again, and before long all six of the kittens were safely on the ground.

Then the little girl found an old basket, without a handle. She carefully put all the kittens into it, and, with the mother-cat trotting beside her, she went out of the barn and back to Mrs. White's house.

How delighted Mrs. White was to have her kittens back again safe and sound! She was hunting for them everywhere!

"A dog came into the house and frightened the mother-cat," she told Joan. "So I suppose she thought she had better take her kittens somewhere else. They would all have caught cold in that draughty barn. It *is* good of you to take so much trouble, Joan."

"I love animals," said Joan, "especially kittens. You can't think how I'd like a pet of my own. Oh dear, look at my party dress! It's all dirty and I've torn it! I can't go to the party, I'm afraid!"

"Oh, I *am* sorry," said Mrs. White. "Can't you go home and put another frock on?"

"I've only got my school frock besides this," said Joan. "It doesn't matter. I don't mind missing the party if I've rescued your kitten family! I do love them so much!"

So Joan missed the party, for she didn't want to go in her old school frock. She was very sad about it, and Mother was sorry for her. Mrs. White had told Mother how kind Joan had been, so Mother understood all about it.

"Never mind, darling, you shall have an Easter egg," said Mother, so Joan looked forward to that.

She wondered if it would be a chocolate one. She did like chocolate very much.

There *was* a chocolate egg for her—and another egg, too—a most surprising Easter egg! Mother brought it into the dining-room with such a funny smile on her face. It was an *enormous* cardboard egg, red, yellow and blue—and it made a noise!

It did really! And what sort of a noise do you think it made? Guess!

It *mewed*! Joan gave a scream of excitement and split the egg in half—and out jumped the dearest, prettiest little Persian kitten you ever saw! It was one that Joan had rescued from the barn that week!

"Mrs. White said that you were just the right person to have one of her kittens," said Mother. "Do you like your Easter egg, Joan?"

"Mother, it's the loveliest one in all the world!' cried Joan. "Oh, I don't mind missing the party if I have a kitten of my own. I am *so* happy!"

Wasn't it a surprising Easter egg?

GUESS THIS ONE!

My first is in chatter. but not in talk,
My second's in trot, but isn't in walk,
My third is in duckling, but isn't in chick,
My fourth is in rapid and also in quick,
My fifth is in Scotland, but not in a Scot,
My sixth is in tangle, but isn't in knot.
My seventh's in baby and also in youth,
My last is in falsehood, but isn't in truth,
My whole is a time that all children adore,
You won't be long guessing the answer, I'm sure

(*Answer:* Holidays.)

EASTER

"Easter!" sings the blackbird, his glossy back a-gleam,
"Easter!" calls the wagtail, by the bubbling stream,
And every little chaffinch cries, "Pink-pink-pink!
We will nest for Easter in a chink-chink-chink!"

"New fur coats for Easter," say the bunnies as they hop,
"And we needn't buy them in a shop-shop-shop!"
"We will curl our whiskers!" squeak the small field-mice,
"Easter-time is coming, and we must look nice!"

"We'll be there for Easter!" sing the swallows, flying fast.
"Easter!" says the cuckoo. "The winter's gone at last!"
Come along, you chiff-chaffs, hurry, willow wren,
We must be back for Easter, it *is* so lovely then!"

THE TALE OF WATTLE WEASEL

ONE time all the animals took to living together—all except Brer Rabbit, and they wouldn't have him with them because they said he was too fond of playing tricks. Now they were all very fond of butter, and they used to put it into the dairy to keep cool—and somehow somebody got in, day after day, and nibbled their precious butter.

"It's a mighty tiresome thing!" said Brer Fox. "We must watch and see who it is." So they watched, and they found some tracks—and they knew that they were Wattle Weasel's.

"We must keep a watch for Wattle Weasel," said Brer Wolf. "Brer Mink, you can go on guard first—and mind this—if you let Wattle Weasel get the butter, then *you* won't have any for a whole year!"

Then the creatures went off to work and left Brer Mink on guard. Well, he sat there and listened and he listened and sat there—and presently along came Wattle Weasel and popped under the door.

"Heyo, Brer Mink!" he cried. "You look cold sitting there. Come and have a game of hide-and-seek!"

Well, Brer Mink loved a game, so off they went, and they played hide-and-seek for hours. Then they sat down to rest, and Brer Mink was so tired that he fell asleep at once. Then, of course, Wattle Weasel ran in and nibbled up the butter. How angry the animals were when they came and found it gone!

The next thing they did was to set Brer Possum on guard. Pretty soon in came Wattle Weasel, grinned at Brer Possum and ran over to him. He gave him a punch in the ribs and began to tickle him. Well, Brer Possum was mighty ticklish and he began to laugh. Wattle Weasel tickled him again and he laughed more loudly, and he got worse and worse the more Wattle Weasel tickled him. He rolled over on the ground, and got so out of breath that he couldn't do a thing—and Wattle Weasel left him and went and nibbled up the butter.

Well, after that Brer Coon was put on guard, and Wattle Weasel came along and grinned and said, "I can run faster than you, Brer Coon!" and he set out over the fields at top speed with Brer Coon after him. But presently Wattle Weasel turned back, took a short cut to the dairy, and nibbled up the butter long before Brer Coon was back.

So then Brer Fox was set to watch the butter, and what did Wattle Weasel do but drive some pheasants along outside the dairy wall, so that Brer Fox could here them calling. "Huh!" said Brer Fox, "Pheasants! Well, it won't do any harm if I go out and catch one!" And out he went after the pheasants, just as Wattle Weasel slipped in at the other door to nibble up the butter.

Well, when the creatures saw that even Brer Fox was tricked by Wattle Weasel they began to be worried.

"Whatever shall we do?" said Brer Bear. "Our butter is always gone when we want it."

"Send for Brer Rabbit," said Brer Mink. "I guess he'll be able to settle Wattle Weasel for us!"

So they sent for Brer Rabbit. But Brer Rabbit thought they were laying a trap for him, and he wouldn't come—and it was only after a lot of begging that he said he would see what he could do.

So he set out for the dairy, humming a little song.

If he couldn't trick Wattle Weasel his name wasn't Brer Rabbit!

Well, Brer Rabbit went down to the dairy, and looked round. He saw the butter and guessed he wouldn't let Wattle Weasel have so much as a taste of it. He felt in his pocket and took out a length of string. Then he hid himself in a corner and waited for Wattle Weasel.

It wasn't long before Wattle Weasel came along, and just as he was going to get the butter, Brer Rabbit yelled out at him. "Don't you eat that butter now!"

Wattle Weasel jumped and looked round. He had a good look at Brer Rabbit and then bowed politely.

"You must be Brer Rabbit!" he said.

"I guess I am," said Brer Rabbit. "Don't you dare to nibble up that butter!"

"Can't I have just a little taste, Brer Rabbit?" said Wattle Weasel.

"Not so much as the scrape of a whisker," said Brer Rabbit.

"Very well," said Wattle Weasel. "What about us having a race? I guess I'd beat you!"

"I'm too tired to race," said Brer Rabbit.

"Well, let's play a nice game of hide-and-seek," said Wattle Weasel.

"I'm too old for that," said Brer Rabbit.

"Well, what *shall* we do?" said Wattle Weasel. "Let's have a game of *some* sort, Brer Rabbit, for goodness' sake!"

"We'll have a tug-of-war, if you like," said Brer Rabbit. "I'll tie the end of this string to your tail and you can tie the other end to *my* tail. Then we'll pull and see who's got the strongest tail!"

Well, Wattle Weasel knew what a feeble little tail Brer Rabbit had—but he didn't know what clever tricks Brer Rabbit's head had! So he said yes, they'd play that game, and Brer Rabbit tied one end of the string to Wattle Weasel's tail, and Wattle Weasel tied the other end to Brer Rabbit's tail.

"Now you stand *in* the dairy," said Brer Rabbit, "and I'll stand outside, and we'll pull against one another with our tails!"

So Brer Rabbit slipped outside—but no sooner was he outside the door than he untied the string from his tail and slipped it round a tree-root! "Pull!" he yelled to Wattle Weasel.

And Wattle Weasel pulled! How he pulled! He tugged till his tail nearly came off. Brer Rabbit peeped through a crack and nearly died of laughing to see him. At last Wattle Weasel couldn't pull any more and he shouted out to Brer Rabbit:

"Come and undo my tail, Brer Rabbit, because you've won the game."

But Brer Rabbit didn't move. He just sat there and grinned, waiting for all the other animals to come home from work. And when they came hurrying along to see if their butter was safe, what did they see but old Wattle Weasel safely tied up by the tail with string, and Brer Rabbit sitting by him as cool as a cucumber!

And my, what a fuss they made of Brer Rabbit! He got half the butter for a reward, and didn't he grin when he ran off home with it that night! It's hard to trick old Brer Rabbit!

A PUZZLE

WHAT ARE THESE TWO THINGS?

I'm what you spread
Upon your bread,
But add a fly to me
And see,
I'll flutter by your head!
But if instead
You add the cup
From which you sup,
Oh, then I'll grow in golden row
In fields and meadows where you go!

(*Answers:* Butter-fly; Butter-cup.)

THE ADVENTURER

He was a spider, yellow and small,
Not long out of the golden ball
In which he was cradled, snug and tight,
With a hundred others, hidden from sight.
Now see him alone on a bramble leaf,
Embarked on adventures beyond belief!
He spins a thread of gossamer fine,
A long and shimmering silken line,
That floats high up in the golden air
Growing longer and longer there
As the spider spins out the thread below;
And now in safety he may let go
His clinging hold of the bramble spray,
And, borne by his life-line, float away,
A tiny speck in the morning light,
Carried away on his gossamer light.
Far he travels, then hauls in his thread
And drops down gently to field or bed,
Seeking a cranny to call his own
Where he may weave and spin alone.

Little spider, adventurer bold,
Good hunting to you, before you grow old!

DID YOU EVER HEAR SUCH A THING?

BETTY, Alice and John had been given three little wooden nesting-boxes to hang up in their garden to see if the birds would build their nests there. Each little box had a roof that could be lifted up so that the children might see if any bird was building inside. It was so exciting to peep.

There was a small round hole in the front of each box for the bird to pop in and out, and Betty, Alice and John did so hope that the blue-tits in their garden would each choose a box for themselves and bring up a family of fluffy blue and yellow babies there.

"There are so many tits in the garden," said Betty. "They have come for our coco-nut all the winter. They know we are their friends, so I expect they will be sure to build in our boxes. I'm going to hang my box in the lilac bush. I am sure little birds would like to nest there. The lilac smells so sweet in the spring."

"I shall put mine on the trunk of the oak tree," said John. "Daddy hung his old one there last year and the tits found it at once. Where will you put yours, Alice?"

"I shall put it by my bedroom window," said Alice, who was the youngest. "Then I shall hear the tits as soon as I wake up in the morning."

"That's a silly place!" said Betty. "Birds don't like to nest where they can easily be seen. Your box will be empty, and ours will be full of baby birds."

"Mine will be full too," said Alice. "I do want to hang my box by my window."

One morning Betty came running indoors in the greatest excitement. "Mummy! Alice! John! The birds have found my box in the lilac bush! When I lifted up the lid this morning I saw tiny twigs and moss at the bottom of the box. And I saw a little blue-tit nearby bringing some more moss in its mouth! Oh, Mummy, I shall have a bird-family in my box!"

Alice ran to look at hers; but there was no sign of any bird building there. She begged a bone from cook and carefully hung it under the nesting-box, hoping that when the tits came to feast on the bone, they might be tempted to hop inside the box and decide on it for a nesting-place.

The next day John came tearing indoors, his face red with delight.

"Mummy! Alice! Betty! *My* box is being built in too! Oh, goody, goody, goody! I *saw* the tit hopping into the little hole, and when I looked inside, there was a nest half-made. Oh, I'm so excited!"

"That's two boxes chosen!" cried Betty. "Alice was silly to put hers by her window. We told her the birds wouldn't build there. Now she won't have a bird-family of her own."

Alice was upset. She shook her head obstinately and said: "I *will* have a bird-family, I tell you! I shall have a piece of coco-nut underneath this very day, as well as the bone. Then they will come. I love the birds and they love me. They will come and build in my box soon." But they didn't! Wasn't it disappointing for Alice? She looked inside her box every single day—sometimes three or four times a day—but never a bit of moss was there! Betty and John showed her their nests—such cosy, mossy little homes inside their boxes. And one day Betty came dancing into the house, shouting: "Mummy! There's an egg in my nest! Mummy, the family has begun!"

And then John's tit laid eggs too, and after that they hatched out into tiny, tiny birds, and the two children were full of delight. Mummy told them to be sure not to peep inside when the big tits were there in case they became frightened and deserted the babies—but the birds knew the children well and were not a bit afraid.

Alice was very sad. No bird built in her box. Mummy said she wasn't to worry, it was only because she had put it in a foolish place. But Alice shook her head.

"It's because they don't love me," she said. "They love Betty and John, but they don't love *me*. And I have always been kind to them. I am very unhappy."

"Don't be a baby!" Mummy said, and kissed her. "Next year they will build in your box. You shall put it in the lilac bush!"

"Next year is a long time away," said Alice. "I wanted them *this* year!"

The little girl was really upset. Mummy didn't know what to do with her because she moped about the garden and wouldn't laugh any more. Betty and John offered to share their bird-families with her but she wouldn't hear of it.

"I want the birds to love me too," she said.

And then a very strange thing happened. Alice went to get her doll's pram out of the summer-house to clean it, because she hadn't played with it for a long time. As she moved it, a bird flew out and startled her. Alice looked into the pram—and then she gave a cry of surprise and delight.

There was a robin's nest built right inside the pram hood, which was up to keep out the damp! Just imagine that! There it was, a dear little cup-shaped nest, made of twigs, roots, and dead leaves, and lined softly with hairs from Spot the dog and Tibs the cat! Inside the nest were five eggs with red-brown spots.

Alice shrieked with joy. She took hold of the pram handle and wheeled her pram carefully to the house, shouting loudly all the way: "Mummy! Betty! John!

Look, look, look! The birds love me very much! I've got a bird-family too!"

"Alice! What do you mean?" Cried Mummy, coming to the door.

"Mummy, the robins have made their nest in my doll's pram!" shouted the excited little girl. "And they've laid five eggs there—such pretty ones! I've brought them to show you!"

"Oh, darling! How lovely for you!" said Mummy. "But you had better take your pram back to the summer-house or the robins will be anxious about their nest."

"But they built it in my pram so that I could take my bird-family for walks," said Alice. "I shall take them for a walk every day!"

"Oh no, darling, you must really leave your pram in the summer-house," said Mummy. "You wouldn't like the robins to desert their nest, would you?"

"Oh, they won't," said Alice. "I'll only take the nest for a *little* walk, Mummy. Oh, I'm so happy. This is much better than having a family in a box. John! Betty! Aren't I lucky to have a nest in my doll's pram?"

"Yes, you are," said John and Betty.

The eggs hatched out into tiny nestlings whose feathers grew quickly. Alice takes them for a tiny walk in the pram each day—and do you know, once the mother robin stayed in the nest all the time too—so she went for a walk as well!

"She trusts me and loves me," said Alice happily. "This is the nicest bird-family in all the world!"

She *was* a lucky little girl, wasn't she?

FOUR BIRDS SPEAK—WHAT ARE THEIR NAMES?

1. In my name you will find something to shoot high in the air.
2. In my name you will find something in which to keep corn.
3. In my name you will find something that will unlock a door.
4. In my name you will find what Humpty Dumpty sat on.

(*Answers:* Sparrow; Robin; Turkey; Swallow.)

MISTER RAT was a horrid fellow, cruel and cunning. He was always hungry, and he loved to find the nests of the birds and eat their eggs or young ones; he loved to sniff out the nest of the little dormice and gobble up their babies; he would even pounce on a young rabbit if it was all alone.

Mowdie the mole walked along the bottom of the ditch, weeping. She did not often walk above ground, for she loved to tunnel below the earth—but this morning she forgot about burrowing, and scuffled along in the ditch.

"What is the matter?" asked Bobtail the rabbit, putting his pretty head out of a hole nearby.

"Oh, oh, Mister Rat has found my nest in the field," wept Mowdie Mole. "And he has eaten all my new little babies; he hasn't left me even one!"

"The wicked fellow!" said Bobtail, his nose woffling up and down. "It is time he was punished!"

"He should be eaten up himself!" said Spiky the hedgehog, uncurling himself where he lay at the bottom of the ditch. "I would eat him myself if I could find him! Yes, I would!"

There came the sound of a laugh in the hedge and all three creatures stiffened with fear. They knew that squealing laugh—it was the snicker of the rat himself!

"So you would eat me yourself, would you?" said Mister Rat, putting his long nose out of the hedge. "Come along then, Spiky—come and eat me—or you, Bobtail—or you, Mowdie Mole! I'm here!"

Bobtail the rabbit disappeared down his hole. Mowdie Mole dug a tunnel in the ditch and sank into it as quick as lightning. Spiky the hedgehog curled himself up tightly and lay there quite still. The rat ran out and sniffed at him.

"You would not be so bold if you hadn't your armour of prickles," he said to the hedgehog. "I will go and tell the fox to come and get you."

He ran off. Spiky was full of fear. He did not like the fox, because Reynard could make him uncurl by making himself smell so horrid that, in disgust, the hedgehog felt he must crawl away; and as soon as he uncurled himself to crawl away from Reynard's dreadful smell the fox would seize him!

Spiky hurried away and hid himself in a hole in the

bank. It was only just big enough for him, and had a ferny curtain hiding the entrance. He felt safe there.

Mister Rat snickered softly to himself as he ran about the hedge and slunk over the fields. He was King of the Countryside! He was Lord of all the creatures of the hedge and ditch! Soon there would be dozens more rats, for in nests here and there young ones were growing up. Aha! Mister Rat would teach them how to hunt for the nests of young mice—for the soft-spined young hedgehogs—for the nestlings in the hedges—for the lizards that darted about the sunny side of the bank—and even for the frogs that lived in the long green grass by the pond.

Mister Rat was very fond of eggs. He had sucked dozens that he had found in nests in the hedgerow. He knew how to glance upwards as he ran along the hedge bank, and spy nests hidden cleverly here and there. Then up he would climb, stick his sharp grey nose into the nest and gobble up the eggs there. Many a robin, thrush, and blackbird had come back in haste to her nest and had found all her eggs gone.

Mister Rat even went down to the farm and stole the eggs in the hen-house. He had many ways of doing that. He would slink into the house through a hole he knew well, and suck an egg in the nesting-box. He would perhaps take one away with him too, to store it in his hole! It was marvellous the way he managed to get it out of the nest without breaking it! Then he would roll it over and over to the hole he had entered by. He would push it through this hole and then roll the egg to his nest. Sometimes two rats stole the eggs together. Then one would turn on his back and hold the egg, and the other would pull him along. Ah, Mister Rat was the cleverest creature in the kingdom!

But one day he made a great mistake.

He was looking out for eggs as usual. He had eaten two belonging to the hedge-sparrow. They were as blue as the sky, but very small. The rat swallowed them but still felt hungry. He wondered if there were any eggs in the hole in the ash tree that stood at the corner of the field. He knew it was partly hollow inside. Once a squirrel had nested there. Then Mister Rat had had a fine feast of young squirrels!

Once a woodpecker had nested there, and Mister Rat had eaten every egg she had laid till in despair she left the tree and flew away to the pinewood on the hill.

Yes—Mister Rat would see if any bird had nested in the ash tree this year! He ran to it, slinking along in the nettles that grew in the ditch. He climbed nimbly up the trunk. It was night-time, but the moon was out, and Mister Rat could see quite well. He came to the entrance of the hole. He sat there and sniffed.

Yes! Some bird was nesting there! The nest smelt of bird. Mister Rat caught sight of something white in the hole. An egg. He slipped down and got it. It was good! But only one egg! How disappointing! Never mind, perhaps there would be others in a day or two.

There were! In two days there was another egg. Mister Rat ate that. In a week's time there was another. Mister Rat ate that. Four days after that there was another—and Mister Rat had that too.

Now the bird who owned the hole in the ash tree that year was a Little Owl. She was puzzled to find that her eggs disappeared so mysteriously. She was a young Little Owl and had never laid eggs before. She told her mate about it, and he hissed solemnly.

"Someone has been stealing them," he said. "Maybe it is the grey squirrel. He is a robber. Or maybe it is the thieving jackdaw. He loves other birds' eggs. We will find out."

It was the dormouse who told the Little Owl who the robber was.

"It is Mister Rat," said the little dormouse, from the shelter of the hedge. "Do not catch me, Little Owl, for I come to warn you of the robber. He stole my own little ones before they even had their eyes open. No one is safe—not even you, Little Owl."

The Little Owls hissed angrily. So that was the robber who had stolen their eggs. This must be seen to.

"Are there many rats here?" said the owls.

"Oh, very many," answered the frightened dormouse. "His families are all growing well now—soon there will be a hundred and more rats running about here—and we will all have to flee away. But they will follow us, so we shall be no better off."

The owls hissed again and flew away. They knew what they were going to do. They flew to the big wood five miles away. Here many Little Owls nested and brought up their young ones—but lately there had been little food for them, because the weasels had been about and had eaten much of the food that the Little Owls wanted for their youngsters.

The two Little Owls called their friends. "Wee-oo, wee-oo, koo-wee-oo!" they called. "Koo-wee-oo!"

"Tvit, tvit!" answered their friends, and from far and near the Little Owls flew down to the tree where sat the two who had come from the far-away wood.

"Wee-oo, wee-oo!" said the two owls. "We come to tell you of much food in a wood far off. Bring your little ones there as soon as they are grown. There are rats by the score in the wood we know."

"We will come!" cried the owls. "Tvit, tvit!"

So in three weeks' time when the young rats were

half grown and were filling the countryside with fear and panic, a great flock of Little Owls came to the wood nearby. With them they brought their half-fledged youngsters, still downy, but with claws that could shut like a trap.

"Wee-oo, wee-oo!" called the Little Owls, as they flew about the wood. They saw the grass move a little in the pale moonlight—down swept an owl, and fixed a young rat in its claws. The rat squealed but could not get away. Another owl dropped like a stone on to a full-grown rat and it had not even time to squeal.

"Tvit, tvit! We have feasted well!" cried the owls that night, as they flew to trees to hide away for the daytime.

Mister Rat was scared to find that so many owls were about. But he said to himself: "Am I not King of the Countryside, and Lord of the Hedgerow? I am afraid of nobody!"

He had a fine wife, and she had a litter of seven small rats that Mister Rat was proud of. His wife would only let him peep at them, for she was afraid he might eat them. Rats did eat their own children sometimes, she knew. Mister Rat ran to warn her to keep close hidden.

The next night a Little Owl saw a movement in the grass near the pond. He pounced—and there was a scuffle! He had caught mother-rat—and nearby in the hole he could hear the little ones squealing! He hooted to his comrades, and in a trice they came and ate up all the young rats.

And then it was Mister Rat who ran along the ditch wailing and weeping for his lost family. But no one heeded him or comforted him. The rabbit was glad. The mole laughed. The hedgehog grunted and said to himself: "Do as you would be done by, Mister Rat!

You are being served the same way as you served us!"

There was a squeal in the night. A Little Owl had caught Mister Rat himself! Ah, Mister Rat, that's the end of you!

"So it was you who ate all my eggs, was it!" cried the Little Owl, as she held Mister Rat in her sharp claws.

"Let me go and I'll never do such a thing again!" squealed the frightened rat.

"You will never do such a thing again anyhow!" said the owl, and she ate him up.

That was the end of Mister Rat—and as for the few rats that were left, they fled from that part of the country in terror. And now the rabbit, the mole, the mice, and the hedgehogs go about in peace and happiness. Aha, Mister Rat, you were a bit too clever when you ate the eggs of the Little Owl!

A PUZZLE

HALF of me you'll see in the corn,
Or, if you look, on your own little head;
The other half is usually worn
By wise old judges in robes of red;
The whole of me is an insect brown
With gauzy wings 'neath a polished back.

Please guess my name and write it down—
Who will be first now, Jill or Jack?

(*Answer:* Ear-wig.)

THE WEATHER FLOWER

I'm the flower that tells the weather,
For, when rain's about,
All my petals shut together
Till the sun comes out.

You'll find me by the laneside growing
With my stars of red,
But when rain-winds come a-blowing
How I hide my head!

Take up all my stalks unruly,
Plant me in a pot,
And I'll tell the weather truly,
Wet or dry or hot!

I'm a very little flower,
Scarlet pimpernel,
Yet the weather, sun or shower,
For you I can tell!

BRER RABBIT GETS THE MEAT

ONCE Brer Rabbit was walking down the high road, feeling mighty hungry, when whom should he come up with but old Brer Bear. And on his shoulder Brer Bear was carrying a big piece of meat!

"This looks good to me," said Brer Rabbit to himself. He shouted to Brer Bear. "Heyo, Brer Bear! I'll walk along with you. How are you feeling this morning?"

"Pretty good," said Brer Bear, putting his meat on the shoulder farthest away from Brer Rabbit. "How do you feel yourself?"

"Oh, I'm the same old one-and-sixpence," said Brer Rabbit. He trotted along by Brer Bear's side, chattering away as he went. But soon he began to sniff—and sniff—and sniff.

"Have you got a bad cold?" asked Brer Bear.

"No," said Brer Rabbit. "But I'm smelling a bad smell, Brer Bear. Is that meat of yours good?"

"Good! Of course it's good!" said Brer Bear angrily.

"Well, it smells pretty bad to me," said Brer Rabbit. "I'll walk on the other side of the road, if you don't mind, Brer Bear. And I'll have to hold my nose. Really, that meat of yours is enough to poison a whole family!"

Brer Rabbit went to the other side of the road, and held his nose tightly. Brer Bear didn't like it at all. At last he put his meat down, and looked at Brer Rabbit.

"If my meat is as bad as all that, what shall I do about it?" he asked.

"Well," said Brer Rabbit, still holding his nose, "I've heard folks say that the best way to cure bad meat is to tie it on a string and drag it through the dust. They do say that the freshness comes back to it that way.

You can easily wash the dirt off afterwards."

"Well, I'll do that," said Brer Bear. "Have you got any string, Brer Rabbit?"

Brer Rabbit had a very long piece in his pocket. "It's *too* long," said Brer Bear.

"Oh, you need a long piece," said Brer Rabbit. "You want to put a good distance between yourself and the smell, don't you, Brer Bear?"

Well, Brer Rabbit tied the meat on to one end of the string and gave the other end to Brer Bear to pull. Then Brer Rabbit picked a bracken leaf from the hedge and ran to the meat. "I'm just going to walk by it as you pull it, and brush the flies off with this leaf," he shouted to Brer Bear.

Well, Brer Bear started to pull that meat through the dust, and Brer Rabbit walked along by it, a good way behind, brushing away with his leaf. Brer Bear kept looking behind, and Brer Rabbit was always there. But when Brer Bear turned a corner, Brer Rabbit took a rock and, quick as lightning, he tied it to the string, cut off the meat, and left it lying in the road. Then on he went, beside the rock, brushing away. Brer Bear saw him there when he next looked behind. Then they came to another corner. But when Brer Bear looked behind again, where was Brer Rabbit? He was nowhere to be seen! He had gone back to where he had left the meat—and there was old Brer Bear, pulling along the big rock and panting and puffing in the sun!

Oh, wicked Brer Rabbit, you'll be caught one day! No doubt about that!

CAN YOU DO THIS?

THIS is a new kind of puzzle. I shall give you eight words, and in each you will find the name of something. For instance, if I give you the word DONG, and tell you to take one letter away and find a pet, you would take the letter N, and find that you had DOG left. Now see if you can do the puzzle yourself:

1. Take two letters from the word SCANT and find an animal.
2. Take one letter from FIRE and find a tree.
3. Take two letters from HEALTHIER and find a flower.
4. Take one letter from COLD and find a fish.
5. Take one letter from STARTLING and find a bird.
6. Take two letters from BANANA and find a girl's name.
7. Take four letters from the word THOROUGH and find a boy's name.
8. Take two letters from SPEAR and find a vegetable.

(*Answers:* Cat; Fir; Heather; Cod; Starling; Anna; Hugh; Pea.)

A CALM DAY

BLUE is the sky, and still are the trees,
Not a leaf stirs in the whispering breeze,
Even the tiny clouds far overhead
Sleep in their places as if they're in bed;
Only the murmuring bees are awake,
As from the flowers the pollen they shake;
Calm is the day, and happiness fills
Valleys and meadows and far-away hills.

A TINY PUZZLE

I'VE a great big mouth, but I never eat,
I've a long, long bed, but I never rest,
I run all day, yet I have no feet,
Pray tell me my name—now who has guessed?

(*Answer:* River.)

THE TAIL THAT WOULDN'T WAG

HIDDEN in the thick creeper on the roof of an old thatched house was a wagtails' nest. It belonged to two wagtails, a cock and a hen. In the nest they had one baby, a fine youngster, with the most piercing voice you ever heard. In fact, it was so loud that the robin, who had a nest nearby, flew up to the wagtails in fear.

"If your nestling calls so loudly, the cats will hear and come up to find him," they said. "Then perhaps they will find *our* nest too, and eat up all our four young ones."

"We can't stop our youngster from making such a noise," said the wagtails. "He is the finest, biggest, strongest wagtail in the world. Look at him!"

The robins looked. They were most astonished to see such a large wagtail. He quite filled the nest, and his long tail stuck over the edge. He opened his orange-coloured mouth and cried so piercingly that the hen robin went off to get a caterpillar for him. He was always hungry—and even seemed to like the hairy, woolly-bear caterpillars that no other bird could eat. The robins often brought him food to make him quiet, but no matter how many grubs both the wagtails and the robins brought him, it made no difference—he squeaked just as piercingly!

When he left the nest—because he had become far too big for it—the wagtails showed him off proudly to all the other birds. They looked at the great nestling in astonishment.

"He doesn't wag his tail as you do," said the bright-eyed blackbird. "Why is that?"

"Oh, we are going to teach him," said the hen wagtail hurriedly. She had not noticed this curious thing—that the fledgling's tail never wagged up and down as theirs did. So all that day the two wagtails tried to show the youngster how to wag his tail. They stood in front of him and nodded theirs a hundred times—up, down, up, down—but although the fledgling did try two or three times, his tail simply would *not* wag!

"It is so disappointing!" said the wagtails. "He is the finest, biggest wagtail we have ever seen—and his tail won't wag!"

"Well, if his tail doesn't wag, he isn't a wagtail," said the thrush.

"Don't be so silly!" cried the hen wagtail, in a fury. "Didn't I bring him up myself, in our own nest? Of course he is a wagtail! I know my own child! His tail will suddenly find how to wag—you will see it one day!"

But the young bird's tail could not wag. He gave up trying, and sat in a tree, still calling loudly for food. He was now so big that the wagtails could not reach up to his beak to feed him—so they had to stand on his shoulder and feed him like that.

The wagtails were most upset about the tail that wouldn't wag, for they were very proud of their enormous child. They called all the birds of the garden around them, and sang to them.

"Chissic, chissic! You *must* say that our youngster is a wagtail—if he isn't, then what *is* he? He must have some sort of name!"

Then a strange thing happened—the young bird made a curious sound in his throat, and then, opening his beak, he called loudly:

"Cuckoo! Cuckoo!"

"A cuckoo!" shouted everyone in great disgust. "No wonder he couldn't wag his tail! He never will!"

And, of course, he never has!

THE KINDLY DOCK

HERE I grow, the common weed
That likes to do a kindly deed.

For if a nettle, green and sly,
Stings you when you're passing by,
Never mind—just hunt for me
And see how comforting I'll be!
Pluck my leaves, so cool and fresh,
Press them on your burning flesh
Where the nettle stung you—and
I'll cool and heal your burning hand!

My name is Dock, the common weed
That likes to do a kindly deed.

BRER RABBIT'S BOAST

Now it happened one morning that Brer Rabbit, Brer Fox and Brer Bear were all going along together, talking mighty biggitty.

"I'm such a strong fellow that if I hug a tree-trunk it squeezes into pulp," said Brer Bear.

"And I'm such a sharp fellow that I can trick Mr. Man as easy as winking!" said Brer Fox.

"What about *you*, Brer Rabbit?" asked Brer Bear, seeing that Brer Rabbit didn't say anything at all, which was rather strange—for if anyone could talk biggitty it was old Brer Rabbit!

"Huh!" said Brer Rabbit, curling up his whiskers. "*You* may be strong, Brer Bear, and *you* may be sharp, Brer Fox—but I'm the man that makes things happen! Did you hear that storm last night? Well, I wanted rain for my beans, so I got the storm to come. And did you notice the tree that fell down over there last week? Well, it was in my way, so I just blew and it fell the next night!"

Brer Fox and Brer Bear stared at Brer Rabbit.

"That's nonsense," said Brer Fox. "You just *can't* make things happen like that, Brer Rabbit."

"Oh, can't I!" said Brer Rabbit. "You be careful, Brer Fox, or I'll make your whiskers grow green!"

Now as they walked, they came to where the railway line ran close by the wood, and in the distance Brer Fox saw a train coming along at top speed.

"See that train, Brer Rabbit!" he said. "Well, seeing that you are such a smart fellow, blow a little and make it stop right here!"

Well, Brer Rabbit was properly caught. He just couldn't do anything else but stand by the railway line and blow like this—phewf! The train came tearing along, rumbling and clattering—and, bless us all, just as it got to where Brer Rabbit, Brer Fox and Brer Bear stood, it gave a frightful, screeching whistle, and stopped with a shriek of brakes! You see, there was a signal not far off, and it was up—so the driver had to stop! It was nothing to do with Brer Rabbit at all!

Well, Brer Fox and Brer Bear gaped and gaped at the stopped train. And Brer Rabbit stared at it, and felt a bit funny. He had blown like that—phewfff! And the train had stopped! How extraordinary!

"Phewffff!" said Brer Rabbit again, just to see what happened. And, at that moment, the signal dropped, and the train whistled again and rumbled off.

Brer Fox and Brer Bear stared at Brer Rabbit, and went rather green about the nose. They were terrified. Whatever would Brer Rabbit do next? Brer Fox slipped off without a word. Brer Bear lumbered away without even a good-bye. They didn't want Brer Rabbit to blow "Phewfff" at them! No, indeed they didn't!

Brer Rabbit went off home, too—and every now and again he stopped and blew—phewff—at a tree or at a bush. But to his great surprise nothing happened.

"I suppose it comes and goes," said Brer Rabbit, puzzled. "My! I guess Brer Fox and Brer Bear won't like it when they see me blowing anywhere near *them*!"

And for a long time after that Brer Rabbit had only got to purse up his mouth and go "phewfff!" to send everyone scuttling off like frightened hens! Cunning old fellow, isn't he!

NIGHT WANDERER

HE wanders all alone at night,
Eating beetles at one bite,
Doesn't mind a slug or two,
Gobbles grubs the whole night through;
Enemies he does not fear,
He rolls up tight when they appear,
Outwitting them with spears of brown;
Guess his name and write it down!

(Then write down the first letter of each line and see if you are right.)

SUMMER VISITORS

THE swallows are here, and all day through
They dart in the sky on their wings of blue.

The Nightingale has arrived again,
Each night she sings in the moonlit lane.

The little Flycatcher's here once more,
He's catching flies by the old barn door.

The Willow-Wren's back, and all day long
She sings her dear little warbling song.

The Cuckoo's arrived and he'd like to play
Hide-and-seek with you the whole of the day.

The Swift and the twittering Martin are here,
And the Chiff-chaff is calling his name far and near.

Welcome to all of you, small feathered things,
May Good Fortune follow your fluttering wings!

WHAT AM I?

HALF of me is a bed so small
That only a baby could sleep there at all!
The other half is a heavy weight,
It's used to measure the coal in our grate!
The whole of me on a reel is run—
Tell me my name and the riddle is done!

(*Answer:* Cot-ton.)

THE WRONG DINNER-TIME

MOTHER, may we go and play in the fields at the bottom of the garden to-day?" asked Flo. "It's such a lovely day, and we won't sit down on the damp grass. The little lambs are in the field, and it's fun to watch them."

"Very well," said Mother, "but you must come when I call you. I shall come to the kitchen door and call 'Cuckoo!' loudly—and you must cuckoo back and come straight in to dinner."

"Yes, we promise to do that, Mother," said Gerry. "We won't be a minute late."

Off they went. Gerry took his box of toy soldiers, and Flo took her wooden doll.

"I can put my toy soldiers out on the top of one of the hencoops in the field," said Gerry. "They will look fine, all shining in the sun."

"And I shall take my doll for a walk all round the field and back," said Flo. "I may find one or two primroses by the stream. If I do, Dolly shall wear them in her hat."

Gerry put out all his soldiers one by one and marched them up the coop. They did look grand. Flo took her doll round the field and found four primroses. She was so pleased. She put two in her own hat and two in Dolly's.

"Come and see my soldiers, Flo," shouted Gerry. "They are all in a long line."

Flo ran over to look at them—and just then a sound came to their ears.

"Cuckoo!"

"Goodness! It's dinner-time already!" said Flo, in dismay. "And we've hardly been here any time. Hurry up and put your soldiers away, Gerry. You know what Mother said—we were to come at once."

"All right," said Gerry, and he scooped all his soldiers into the box. He put the lid on, and the two children trotted back home. They went indoors and found Mother washing some cups at the sink.

"What are you back here for?" said Mother, in surprise. "I thought you went to play in the field."

"Well, Mother, you called us in," said Flo. "We came at once."

"Bless us, child, I didn't call you!" said Mother. "It's only twelve o'clock. You've another hour till dinner-time."

"But we *heard* you call us, Mother," said Gerry.

"Well, you heard wrong then," said Mother, wiping the cups dry. "Go along now. I expect it was someone else you heard."

Flo and Gerry ran off again. This time Gerry took his wooden train and Flo took her ball. Soon they were back in the field with the lambs again, and Flo was throwing her ball up and catching it. The lambs came round to watch, and when she missed the ball, so that it went bouncing towards them on the grass, they skipped off on their funny little legs pretending to be quite frightened.

Gerry filled his wooden engine with stones and pretended that he was taking goods from place to place. Just as he was filling it for the third time, he stood up and listened.

"Flo!" he cried. "Time to go home. I heard Mother calling."

"You didn't!" said Flo.

"I did!" said Gerry.

"Didn't!" said Flo.

"Well, listen then and see," said Gerry. So they listened—and, sure enough, Flo heard "Cuckoo!"

"Sorry, Gerry," she said, "you're right. It is Mother—but I didn't think it could possibly be one o'clock."

Back home they went at top speed—and this time Mother was hanging out some clothes in the garden.

"Back again!" she said, in astonishment. "What's brought you home so soon?"

"Mother, but you *called* us again!" said Flo, in the greatest surprise. "You did really. We both heard you."

"Darling, I didn't call you," said Mother. "It is not quite half-past twelve."

"Well, who could it be then, calling us like that?" said Gerry, puzzled.

"Let's go back to the fields and see if we can spy anyone hiding," said Flo. "Oh, Gerry—it might be a fairy! Just playing us a trick, you know!"

They ran back to the field and hunted carefully all round the hedge. Then they heard the voice again, "Cuckoo!"

"There *is* someone hiding nearby," said Flo. "I heard that call again—and I'm sure it's not Mother this time. Oh, do let's find whoever it is, Gerry."

But although they hunted everywhere, not a boy or a girl or a pixie could they see, not one. It was most disappointing.

"Cuckoo! Cuckoo!" The children heard a voice in the distance and saw Mother waving to them.

"It *is* Mother this time!" said Flo. "Come on, Gerry."

They ran home for the third time—and it *was* Mother calling them. As they washed their hands they told Mother how puzzled they were. As they were telling her, a voice called clearly, not far off: "Cuckoo!"

"Did you hear that?" said Flo excitedly. "Mother, do you suppose it's a fairy having a joke?"

Mother laughed till the tears ran down her face. "My dears," she said, "what silly-billies you are! That's the cuckoo come back again for the summer!

He's been calling all the morning! Did you really think it was I who was calling so often?"

"The cuckoo!" cried the children in delight, and rushed to the door at once. Sure enough, it was—they heard his clear double-call coming down the hillside: "Cuckoo! Cuckoo!"

"Cuckoo!" the children shouted back. "You tricked us this morning, Cuckoo, and made us go home twice for nothing—but we're very glad you are back again!"

"Cuckoo!" shouted the cuckoo—and they heard him all the time they were having dinner. He was just as glad to be back as they were glad to have him!

THE CUCKOO

I'M here again! Cuckoo, cuckoo!
  Have you heard my call?
Of all the birds that come to you
  I'm welcomed most of all!
I am a sly and lazy bird,
  I never build a nest,
But when my double-note is heard
  I'm sure you like it best.
You rarely see me flying near,
  You do not know me well,
And yet you welcome me each year,
  Though why, I cannot tell!
Perhaps you'll come with me and play
  At hide-and-seek—oh do!
I love to hide myself away
  And call "Cuckoo!" Don't you?

HIDDEN TOYS

You will find six hidden toys in the following sentences.

1. Scrub all the floors, please.
2. Don't wake up Daddy from his nap.
3. Dab a tiny spot of paint on it.
4. I am going to put it away.
5. If it rains I shall stay in.
6. You can pack it easily.

(*Answer!* ball; snap; bat; top; train; kite.)

BRER RABBIT AND BRER TERRAPIN

It happened once that Brer Rabbit was caught by a farmer, eating his lettuces. He picked up Brer Rabbit by his long ears, popped him into a sack, tied up the neck and threw him on the ground. "Now you wait there, you little robber, till I go home to my dinner," said the farmer. "Then I'll have you boiled in the pot!"

Well, Brer Rabbit was mighty scared! He lay as still, as still, hoping the man would think he was dead. The man took no notice of him at all, but went into the next field to work, knowing quite well that Brer Rabbit was safe in the sack. Soon Brer Rabbit began to wriggle about in the sack—but it was no good; he was tied up fast this time! He struggled and rolled about, and soon found a little hole in the sack through which he could peep out. He set his eye there and saw Brer Terrapin coming slowly along, carrying his heavy shell on his back. Brer Rabbit lay quite still till Brer Terrapin was nearby. Then he called to him in a hoarse whisper:

"Hist! Brer Terrapin, don't make such a noise with your galumphing feet!"

Brer Terrapin was so startled to hear a voice coming

from the sack that his eyes nearly fell out of his bald head.

"What are you in that sack for?" he asked at last.

"Hush, I tell you!" said Brer Rabbit, again. "I'm hiding. Do you see those green lettuces yonder, Brer Terrapin? Well, as soon as the farmer has gone home I'm going to creep out of this sack and EAT THEM ALL UP! My, what a feast!"

Brer Terrapin's mouth began to water.

"I wish there was room in that sack for me, too," he said, longingly.

"Well, you can come in if you like," said Brer Rabbit very amiably. "Just undo the knot tied round the neck, Brer Terrapin, and slip in beside me."

"My, how did you manage to tie this knot yourself?" wondered Brer Terrapin, chewing it. "You always were a clever one."

"Yes, I always was clever," grinned Brer Rabbit, inside the sack. Soon the knot was broken and the neck of the sack opened wide. Brer Rabbit tried to slip out as Brer Terrapin slipped in.

"Hey, let me come in!" cried Brer Terrapin.

"Keep your shell on, old hardback!" said Brer Rabbit, cheekily. "I'm only making room for you."

He slipped right out and Brer Terrapin got in. Brer Rabbit tied the string in a knot, whilst Brer Terrapin inside the sack began to struggle and cry, "Aren't you a-coming in too, Brer Rabbit?"

"No, there's not really enough lettuce for us both!" said Brer Rabbit, generously. "You can have it all. Good-bye!"

With that off he went, lippitty-clippitty through the fields, leaving poor Brer Terrapin tied up in the sack for the farmer to find. And what an astonished man he was to find a terrapin in his sack instead of the rabbit he had left there earlier in the day!

WHO AM I?

I HAVE no eyes and yet I know
When dark and daylight come and go.
I have no nose and yet can tell
Where food is hidden, by its smell!
I have no ears and yet can hear
When enemies are coming near.
No legs have I, yet swift I go
From place to place, or dart below.
Beneath the earth my home is found
And there I tunnel in the ground.
I lie all day in dirt and gloom,
Quite happy in my cosy room.
Now who am I? Think hard a minute—
Find my hole and see me in it!

(*Answer!* A worm.)

THE BIRD MAN

THERE was once a little boy called Ben, who loved watching the birds that flew among the trees and about the blue sky. He was a little town boy who had just come to live in the country, and very often his school friends laughed at him because he didn't know as much as they did about the flowers and animals of the countryside.

When the swallows came back, Ben watched them flying high in the air, catching the insects. "What are those birds called with forked tails?" he asked his friends. They laughed at him scornfully.

"Don't you know *that*?" they said. "They are swallows!"

"But they are not all swallows, are they?" said Ben, puzzled. "Some of them seem a bit different."

"Don't you believe it!" laughed his friends. "All those birds with forked tails are swallows."

All the same, Ben felt sure some of the birds were different from the others. He was standing in a field watching them one day when a bright-eyed little man came along whistling.

"What are you looking at?" he asked.

"At all those swallows!" said Ben. "They do make such a pretty twittering sound as they fly."

"They are not all swallows," said the little twinkling-eyed man. "There are three different birds up there in the sky! Can't you tell the difference?"

"Not very well," said Ben. "I'm really a town boy."

"*I'll* show you the difference!" said the little man. He began to whistle in a queer twittering manner, A little bird dropped down from the sky and lay quivering in the man's outspread hand.

"Here is the real swallow, the barn-swallow who loves to build in barns and outhouses," said the man. "Look at his steel-blue back his chestnut forehead and throat—and his pale underparts. See his beautiful forked tail!"

The bird flew upwards with a glad twitter, and Ben saw the flash of its pale underparts. The little man again gave a soft twittering whistle and another bird dropped down to his outspread hand. It seemed very like the barn-swallow. The man stroked the little creature lovingly. "This is a cousin of the barn-swallow, the house-martin," he said. "He builds under the eaves of your houses. See his white underparts right up to his beak, and see this white patch at the bottom of his back. You can always tell him by that as he flies. His tail is not so forked as that of the real swallow."

He sent the bird up into the air, and then uttered such a curious screech that Ben jumped. Another bird dropped to his hand, screeching just as the little man had done.

"This is a swift," said the man. "He is not a cousin of the swallow, yet he has the forked tail and sickle-shaped wings you see in them. He is sooty-black all over except for this white spot on his chin. Hear him screech as he goes!"

Up went the little bird, screeching madly. Ben watched him—and then he turned to the bird man. He was gone! It was most mysterious!

"Anyway, I know more than country boys do now!" thought Ben, pleased. "I can point out the swallow, the house-martin and the swift to them, as they fly. Won't they be surprised?"

Can *you* do that too?

WHO CAN DO THIS?

I AM twelve months; behead me and I grow on your head; add another tail and I am a nobleman; add yet another tail and I will never be late; add another head and I hope your teeth look like this; chop off my tail and find me in an oyster; chop off my tail again and I grow on a tree; add another head and I am a dangerous weapon; take away my middle and I am fixed to the mast of a ship; chop off my tail and head and find me in your family.

(*Answer:* Year; Ear; Earl; Early; Pearly; Pearl; Pear; Spear; Spar; Pa.)

BRER RABBIT BORROWS A FIDDLE

IT happened one day that Brer Rabbit had a fancy to play the fiddle. So he borrowed Mr. Benjamin Ram's old fiddle, and away he went into the woods to practise, but it began to rain, and old Brer Rabbit looked about for a place to shelter in.

Not far away was a small house, so into the door Brer Rabbit hopped, and looked around. Now this house belonged to Brer Wildcat, and he wasn't very fond of Brer Rabbit.

So, when he spied him hopping in as bold as sparrows in December, he winked at Mrs. Wildcat, slammed the door and locked it.

"Morning," said Brer Rabbit, not quite liking the look of Brer Wildcat.

"Morning," said Brer Wildcat, and he stretched out all his claws. "Hey, Mrs. Wildcat, put the pot to boil in the kitchen!"

Brer Rabbit didn't like the sound of that. He looked all round, but there was no way of getting out.

"I've filled the pot, so come and help me to lift it over the fire!" shouted Mrs. Wildcat from the kitchen. Brer Wildcat gave Brer Rabbit a nasty grin and ran out.

"Well, maybe if I play them a tune they will feel a bit more friendly to me," said Brer Rabbit, and he pulled at a fiddle string.

"Plink! Plonk! Plunk!" went the fiddle, making a strange noise. Mrs. Wildcat dropped the pot in a fright, and the water spilt over Brer Wildcat's toes. They both listened in fear. Brer Rabbit wasn't much good at playing the fiddle, but he could pull the strings all right with his fingers. "Plink-plonk, plink-plonk!"

Then he tried running the bow over the strings, and that fiddle wailed like a lost cat. Brer Wildcat and

Mrs. Wildcat clutched hold of one another. Brer Rabbit caught sight of them through the door and he suddenly grinned to himself.

"Plink, plonk, plunk! Eeeeeeeee, oooo, aaaah! Plink, plunk, plink, plunk!" What a noise that fiddle made! Then Brer Rabbit called out cheerfully, "Brer Wildcat, I've found your cousin hiding under the table. So I'm scaring the life out of him, I am! Hear him yowl! You come along in, and I'll get hold of you and scare the life out of you, too!"

"Eeeeee-ow-eeeee-oooo! Plink, plonk, plunk!" went the fiddle, as Brer Rabbit scraped the strings and pulled them. Brer Wildcat gave a yowl like the fiddle, caught hold of Mrs. Wildcat, opened the back door and fled away down the garden path as if twenty dogs were after him. Brer Rabbit laughed till he cried. Then he walked out, too, and all the time he pulled at the strings. "Plink, plonk, plunk!"

Far away in the woods came a wailing sound from the two terrified wildcats. Brer Rabbit grinned and stepped the opposite way.

"Your fiddle's better than mine!" he called to them. "Eaaa, ow, eee, aaaah! Wail away, wildcats! Plink, plonk, plunk!"

And off he went, laughing as loudly as a green woodpecker!

RICHES

SILVER Daisy, buttercup gold,
Here they gleam for us all to hold,
Yellow and white the meadows shine,
With silver and gold that is yours and mine!

Treasure that cannot be hidden away,
Gold that nobody's bills will pay,
Wealth that is mine and yours to share,
And store in our memories, rich and rare.

Dance in the meadows—we've gold on our shoe!
Pluck a few daisies—there's silver for you!
We've far more riches than we can hold
With big moon-daisies and buttercup gold!

THE BEE AND THE FLOWER

LITTLE bee,
Little bee,
Won't you come and visit me?
I'm a flower, small and red,
Growing in the garden bed,
And my seeds I want to make,
So your help I'd like to take.
Bring me pollen, little bee,
From a flower just like me!

Little flower,
Little flower,
I'll do all that's in my power!
Here I come on gauzy wing
Pollen powder fine to bring!
But I am a hungry bee—
Have you any food for me?

Little friend,
Little friend,
On my help you may depend.
Nectar sweet for you I'll hide,
Put your little tongue inside,
And you'll find it, hidden deep
In my heart where you may creep!
It is good to help each other,
So I'll feed you, small bee-brother!

A FARMYARD CHARADE

You know what a charade is, don't you? You choose a word, divide it up into syllables, and act each bit, and, last of all, act the whole word. Then people have to guess what the word is. Well, here is a farmyard charade for you to act. Your teacher will read it to you first, and you must see if you can guess the word. Then perhaps you can act the charade for another class!

In the Farmyard

(*The hens are talking.*)

Henny-Penny. Kuk-kuk-kuk-kuk-*kuk*! What do you think, sisters! The farmer says we aren't laying enough eggs! He says he will send us to be roasted for people's dinners!

All Hens. Kuk-kuk-kuk! Wicked man!

Scratch-about. Of course we can't lay eggs unless we are fed properly! Why doesn't he give us more corn to eat?

All Hens. Kuk-kuk-kuk-kuk! Why doesn't he?

Henny-Penny. Ah, if we had more food we could lay fine big eggs every day. Then our nests would always be full of eggs and the farmer would be pleased.

All Hens. Kuk-kuk-kuk-kuk! *Dozens* of eggs!

Scratch-about. Well, shall we go and tell the farmer to give us more corn? Where is he?

All Hens. Kuk-kuk-kuk-kuk! Over in the field.

Henny-Penny. Come along, then, we'll all go to him.

On the Farmyard Wall

(*The hens are singing to the listening farmer.*)

Henny-Penny. Here we sit on the farmyard wall,

ALL HENS. We've come to complain to you, one and all!

SCRATCH-ABOUT. Dozens of eggs for you we'll lay,

ALL HENS. If you'll give us plenty of food each day. Kuk-kuk-kuk-kuk-*kuk*!

HENNY-PENNY. We won't be roasted or cooked in a pan,

ALL HENS. Please hear what we say, kind farmer-man!

FARMER. I won't give you any more food at all! (*Clap hands.*) Shoo, shoo, shoo, from the top of my wall!

(*Hens scatter, crying angrily, Kuk-kuk-kuk-kuk-kuk!*)

* * *

(*The hens run away. They come to a signpost and look at it.*)

HENNY-PENNY. It will serve that bad farmer right when he finds that all his hens have gone!

ALL HENS. Kuk-kuk-kuk-kuk! Wicked man!

SCRATCH-ABOUT. It's all very well to run away—but where are we going to?

ALL HENS. Kuk-kuk-kuk-kuk! Somewhere nice, please!

HENNY-PENNY. Well, look, here's a signpost. Let's see what it says.

ALL HENS (*running up to it*). Kuk-kuk-kuk-kuk! What does it say?

SCRATCH-ABOUT (*reading*). It has three arms. One says, To Devon. One says, To Dorset. And the last says, To Cornwall.

ALL HENS. Kuk-kuk-kuk-kuk! Where shall we go?

HENNY-PENNY. There is good cream in Devon.

ALL HENS. Kuk-kuk-kuk-kuk! Delicious.

SCRATCH-ABOUT. So there is in Dorset.

ALL HENS. Kuk-kuk-kuk-kuk! But we want corn!

HENNY-PENNY. Well, there *must* be corn in *Corn*wall.
Let's go there. Quick march, this way!

ALL (*marching off*):

Kuk-kuk-kuk-kuk,
Hear us all cluck,
We're off to a spot
Where we may find a lot
Of sweet corn to eat.
Ah, what a fine treat!
No wonder we cluck,
Kuk-kuk-kuk-kuk!

(*And now, my dears, what is the word, please?*)

THE LISTENING CORN

THE corn in the field is full of ears,
And it listens the whole day long;
Many and sweet are the sounds it hears,
Whisper, and twitter and song!
It hears the patter of beetles' feet,
The whirr of a ladybird's wings,
The squeal when two little dormice meet,
The sigh when a poppy flings
Her scarlet dress in rags to the ground;
It hears the grasshopper shout,
And the small and busy pattering sound
When the little brown ants are out.
It listens to swallows' twittering cry,
And the lark's song overhead,
It hears the snail go slowly by,
And the spider's hurrying tread.
Even the thistledown's flight it hears,
On the wandering breezes borne—
No sound escapes the thousand ears
Of the watchful, listening corn!

EIGHT HIDDEN ANIMALS. WHAT ARE THEY?

1. Mabel and Harry are doing their homework.
2. You must wash, or Selina will be angry.
3. Long, long ago a tremendous giant lived.
4. The friar and the monk eyed one another closely.
5. When Harry came, Lucy left in a huff.
6. What have you done with my candle? O, pardon me—here it is!
7. Your wash-tub is on the back-door step.
8. To guess all these animals would be a very clever thing to do!

(*Answers:* Eland; Horse; Goat; Monkey; Camel; Leopard; Bison; Beaver.)

BRER BEAR'S STUFFING

It happened one day that Brer Rabbit was boasting as usual, and Brer Fox was laughing at him.

"Laugh as much as you like!" said Brer Rabbit fiercely, doubling up his fists. "But I tell you, Brer Fox, I'm as strong as a lion! I could beat anybody, and send them rolling to the ground."

"Well, you couldn't knock Brer Bear over," said Brer Fox. "He's too big for you, Brer Rabbit."

"I could knock the stuffing out of Brer Bear any day!" boasted Brer Rabbit. "Huh, he's an easy man to fight, he is, for all he is so big. I tell you, Brer Fox, I could knock the stuffing out of him as easy as eating a cabbage leaf!"

Just then Brer Bear passed by and heard all Brer Rabbit's boasting. He was angry, and walked right up to Brer Rabbit and stood in front of him.

"All right, Brer Rabbit," he said, "you knock the

stuffing out of me! Go on! I'd like to know what my stuffing is, if I've got any. You're a boaster, Brer Rabbit, that's what you are!"

Brer Fox laughed fit to kill himself to see Brer Rabbit's face, but Brer Rabbit soon spoke up.

"Give me leave to go and get my boxing-gloves," he said, "and I'll soon knock the stuffing out of you, Brer Bear, just as I said. But I must have my boxing-gloves, or I'll hurt you too much."

"Never mind about hurting me," said Brer Bear, winking at Brer Fox. "You just go ahead and biff me, Brer Rabbit. I expect it'll just feel as if you're tickling me, but that's all."

Then Brer Rabbit spoke as if he was mighty offended.

"I don't take it kindly of you to doubt my word like this, Brer Bear," he said. "And, if you don't mind, we'll do this thing properly. I'll get my boxing-gloves and you and Brer Fox go round and tell everyone I'm going to knock the stuffing out of you. Then you'll soon see if I'm boasting or not."

"*I'll* go round and tell the folks to come and watch," said Brer Bear, "but Brer Fox can go with you to get your boxing-gloves. I don't trust you any more than I'd trust a cuckoo, Brer Rabbit, and if we let you out of our sight now you'll be off like a streak of lightning and that's the last we'll see of you. Come on, Brer Fox, you go with Brer Rabbit and get his gloves. I'll go and tell everyone to come and watch."

So off went Brer Rabbit and Brer Fox, Brer Rabbit holding his head up and muttering to himself very fiercely, and Brer Fox laughing all the time, thinking Brer Rabbit was nicely caught.

"Huh!" said Brer Rabbit, "*I'll* knock the stuffing out of Brer Bear, you see if I don't, Brer Fox! I'll make him dance and shout. You wait!"

Well, Brer Fox came to Brer Rabbit's house, and Brer Rabbit ran in to get his boxing-gloves. He took his biggest pair of woollen gloves, which were what he called his boxing-gloves, and he ran to the larder with them. He opened the flour-bin and emptied a fistful of flour into each glove. Then he slipped them on his paws and tied them tightly round the wrist.

He ran out to Brer Fox with a mighty big grin on his face and said he was ready. Back they went to where they had left Brer Bear, and there they found Brer Wolf, Brer Hare, Brer Turkey Buzzard, Brer Terrapin and Brer Bull-Frog, all squatting round ready to see the big fight.

"Well, Brer Bear," said Brer Rabbit, strutting up as bold as you please, "are you ready to have the stuffing knocked out of you? I've got my boxing-gloves on, so I won't hurt you more than I can help. Don't you be frightened if you see your stuffing coming out now, will you!"

"Stars and moon!" said Brer Bear impatiently, "haven't you done boasting yet, Brer Rabbit? Come on and biff me as hard as you like. You'll just feel like a fly buzzing round, that's all!"

Brer Rabbit didn't wait a minute longer. He danced right up to Brer Bear and hit him hard with both his gloved paws. Biff!

A cloud of white flour flew out of the gloves! Biff! Blim-blam! Great clouds of flour shot out every time Brer Rabbit hit Brer Bear, and all the folk watching got up on their feet in excitement.

"What's that you're knocking out of Brer Bear?" cried Brer Terrapin in surprise.

"It's just his stuffing, that's all!" cried Brer Rabbit. "Didn't I tell you I'd knock the stuffing out of old Brer Bear? Do you feel all right, Brer Bear? Your stuffing is coming out dreadfully! You'll soon be nothing but a bag of bones!"

Biff! Bam! Brer Rabbit hit as hard as he could and soon the air was full of flying flour. Brer Bear became frightened and tried to get out of Brer Rabbit's way. But Brer Rabbit went after him, gaily hitting him, crying out at the top of his voice, "Here comes your stuffing, Brer Bear! Here it is! Biff! You won't have any stuffing left soon!"

"Don't you hit me any more, Brer Rabbit," said Brer Bear, in a frightened voice. "Stop, now! I'm feeling very queer with all that stuffing coming out. I'm getting thinner, I'm sure I am. Leave me some of my stuffing or I'll drop down and die!"

"I don't want you to do that, Brer Bear," said Brer Rabbit generously, and he stopped after one last hard biff. "Now, then, all you watching folks—who wants a turn with me? You, Brer Fox?"

But Brer Fox and everyone else had gone! My, they *were* afraid of Brer Rabbit that day—and didn't he laugh when he went home! He certainly did!

A ROOF ABOVE HIS HEAD

"I MAY be slow, and stupid too,"
  The crawling tortoise said.
"But still, I'm sharp enough to keep
  A roof above my head!

"You rabbits have to seek your homes
  When enemies are near,
You birds spend hours building nests,
  A new one every year!

"You mice make homes of flimsy grass
That any wind would scatter,
But if a storm blows over mine
It really doesn't matter!

"My home is hard and strong and safe,
It has a splendid roof,
And though it's out in wind and rain
It's always weatherproof!"

A PUZZLE-POEM

HALF of me is an animal sly
(Hear the dogs bark when he goes by!)
And half of me in winter you wear
(Two of them, please, to make a pair!)
Now put my halves together, and lo,
Into a dreaming flower I'll grow,
Swaying tall in the summer breeze,
Loved by the clumsy old bumble-bees!
What am I?

(*Answer:* Fox-glove.)

SEASIDE DAYS

No shoes, no socks,
No shorts, no frocks,
Just a bathing suit so small
It's really hardly there at all,
And a sun-hat when it's hot,
(Though, of course, we'd rather *not*!)

Blue sea, blue sky,
And a breeze that hurries by,
Little waves in twinkling rows
That run to curl round dancing toes,
Big waves that crash and break—
Run away, for goodness' sake!

Wooden spades, tin pails,
Shrimping-nets for catching whales,
Sand in toes and clothes and hair,
In the bed and everywhere!
Oh, it's fun beside the sea
For Gillian, Imogen—and me!

(*Put the names of your own friends in the last line instead of Gillian's and Imogen's.*)

THE BOY WHO WOULDN'T BATHE

ONCE upon a time there was a boy who went to the seaside with his mother and father and sisters and brothers. His name was Thomas, and he had two brothers called Jim and Peter and two sisters called Mary and Joan.

Their mother bought them a bathing-suit each, and their father said he would take them into the sea to bathe every morning. So, when the right time came, Thomas, Jim, Peter, Joan and Mary put on their bathing-suits and ran down to the water. They had paddled that morning, and loved it—but as soon as they got out into the sea above their knees, the water seemed to feel rather cold.

"Ooh! It's too cold to bathe!" said Thomas, shivering. "I'm not going to!"

"Come along!" called his father. "Wade out to your waist, then dip under! It's fine once you're in!"

Jim waded out and dipped under. So did Joan. Peter took a little longer, but under he went at last—and Mary lost her footing and went under without meaning to! So now they were all wet except Thomas.

And will you believe it, Thomas was still only up to his knees in the water! "I don't like it, it's cold!" he wailed, "I'm afraid of the deep sea!"

"Very well," said his father. "Stay where you are. You are behaving like a baby, so you'd better stay where the babies stay—at the edge of the water!"

So Thomas stayed at the edge of the water. He thought he would fetch his boat and sail her—so he did. It was a fine ship—not one of those annoying ones that flop over on to their side and lie there—but a proper one with big white sails. It sailed upright, bobbing up and down beautifully. Thomas held it by a string.

And then the strong wind blew the string out of his hand! His boat fled away from him, away, away on the wind, out to sea!

"Oh, my ship, my ship!" wailed Thomas. But none of the others heard him, for they were all splashing and shouting. Nobody saw the lovely boat sailing away either.

"Come back, ship!" shouted Thomas. But the ship took no notice. It sailed on, right away from Thomas, out towards the deep, deep sea.

Thomas waded after it, crying tears all down his freckled nose. He couldn't bear to lose his beautiful ship. The ship sailed on. Thomas waded out further. He was up to his waist! Did he feel the cold water? No—not a bit! He waded on and on—the sea was up to his shoulders—up to his chin—and then he *just* managed to reach that runaway ship and hold it firmly! A big wave came and Thomas jumped up as it passed him. A little salt water went into his mouth, but he didn't care! He had his precious ship!

"Daddy! Daddy! Look at Thomas! He's out deeper than any of us!" shouted Jim. "He's braver than any of us!"

Daddy looked—and he *was* astonished.

"You're too deep, Thomas!" he shouted. "Go back! I thought you said you were not going to bathe!"

"I'm not bathing!" shouted back Thomas. "I only waded after my ship!"

How all the others laughed! Funny old Thomas—wouldn't go out into the water with his brothers and sisters, but didn't think twice about going up to his chin for his ship!

"Your ship has taught you to bathe!" laughed Mary. And so it had—for Thomas wasn't a baby any more after that!

A SEASIDE RIDDLE-ME-REE

My first is in shingle, and also in sand,
My second's in pierrots, but not in band,
My third is in steamer, but not in its hull,
My fourth is in sea-bird, but isn't in gull,
My fifth is in catfish, but isn't in cod,
My sixth is in line, but isn't in rod,
My seventh's in schooner, and also in ship,
My last is in bathing, but never in dip,
My whole is a creature you'll find on the sand,
With plenty of fingers but never a hand!
What is it?

(*Answer:* Starfish.)

POOR BRER BEAR!

ONCE upon a time Brer Bear went for a walk with Brer Rabbit. Brer Rabbit had his pop-gun with him and a fine supply of corks, which he kept popping off at everyone he met. This made Brer Bear giggle so much that after a bit he forgot to notice which way they were going—and then, of course, the two of them were lost!

"Stars and moon!" said Brer Bear, stopping short and looking all round him. "Where are we? If we aren't lost, Brer Rabbit, I'll eat my whiskers!"

"Oh, don't do that!" said Brer Rabbit. "Let's sit down and lick out that honey-jar you've got with you."

"I've told you before, and now I tell you again," said Brer Bear, "that honey is for my dinner and is nothing to do with you, Brer Rabbit. You won't even get a lick of it, so don't think it, you greedy creature!"

"Let's go down *this* way," said Brer Rabbit, going off down a green path. "Maybe this is right." But it wasn't—and before very long night fell, and it was dark.

"Well, we'd better lie down on the grass and try to sleep," said Brer Rabbit cheerfully. "We can't see our way now, right or wrong!"

So down they lay, Brer Rabbit on his side and Brer Bear on his broad back. Presently he began to snore, and Brer Rabbit frowned—but though he punched Brer Bear hard he wouldn't stop. Then the moon came up, and Brer Rabbit turned on his back and blinked.

Suddenly he saw two great paws quite near, turned over as if they were going to clutch at Brer Bear, and Brer Rabbit's heart gave a big jump. Then he saw that the paws really belonged to Brer Bear himself! They were his big hind-feet sticking up at the end of him, looking for all the world as if they were paws coming to clutch at them. He chuckled to himself, and woke Brer Bear by punching him very hard indeed. "Oooomph!" said Brer Bear. "What's up, Brer Rabbit?" "Sh!" said Brer Rabbit, in a frightened sort of voice. "Look there, Brer Bear! Look at those awful great paws coming to choke us! Ooh! What shall we do?"

Brer Bear caught sight of his hind-feet sticking up in the moonlight, and he was frightened out of his

wits. He shook and shivered and the paws shook and shivered, too. "Brer Rabbit, let's run!" whispered poor Brer Bear.

"That would be cowardly," said Brer Rabbit. "Look, take my pop-gun, Brer Bear. I've put a good cork in it. You shoot at those awful great paws, and whoever they belong to will jump and run for his life. Then we'll be safe!"

Brer Bear took the gun and aimed tremblingly at the paws. POP! The cork shot out, and hit his right hind-paw with a terrible smack!

"WOW!" yelled Brer Bear in pain and fright. He leapt to his feet and made off, howling as if twenty dogs were after him. "He bit me, yes, he did, he bit me! Wow!"

Well, Brer Rabbit lay back and laughed till he couldn't laugh any more. To think of old Brer Bear shooting his own toes! What a joke! But there was an even better joke—for Brer Bear had left behind his jar of honey.

It didn't take Brer Rabbit long to finish it up—then off he went home, lippitty, clippitty, licking his sticky whiskers. As for Brer Bear, he didn't turn up again for three days, and even then he was limping. *Poor* old Brer Bear!

A SEASIDE PUZZLE FOR YOU

(Find the names of the mixed-up seaside creatures!)

THE seaside is a most exciting place. On the rocks we found some pretty Edewase, some of it covered with Smeluss. We tried to pick up a Timpel, but we couldn't even move it. A small Barc ran out of a pool and then ran back again when it saw us. We spied a big Primsh, but could not catch it. It was so big that at first we thought it was a Warnp. We found a beautiful red Mennoea, with a Shelljify floating nearby. We thought our quaintest find was a big Fishrats. All the time we hunted for these treasures we could hear the loud calling of the Sllug.

(*Answers*: Seaweed; Mussels; Limpet; Crab; Shrimp; Prawn; Anemone; Jellyfish; Starfish; Gulls. Did you find them all?)

THE MOUSE AND THE SQUIRREL

THERE was a little mouse who lived in a hole in a ditch. He ran about all night long, looking for titbits everywhere—and one night he went into a cottage and sniffed about for a bit of bacon or piece of cheese.

Aha! What was this? Bacon rind, smelling fresh and delicious! The mouse ran to it and began to nibble.

But alas! It was a trap; and there came a loud rap as the trap worked, and tried to catch the little mouse. He leapt backwards, but his front foot was caught and badly hurt.

The little mouse squealed and pulled his foot away. Then, limping badly, he hurried out of the cottage by the hole through which he had come, and went back to the wood.

His foot made him feel very ill, for it pained him. He could not go out hunting for grain and seeds as he used to do. He was hungry and wondered if he could ask help from someone.

By his hole he saw a fat grey squirrel. The squirrel was sitting up on his hind legs, his bushy tail well in the air, nibbling at an acorn.

"Good day, Squirrel," said the mouse humbly. "Could you spare me an acorn? Or could you get me a scarlet hip from the wild-rose bramble over there? I have hurt my foot and cannot go hunting for food. I am very hungry."

"What!" cried the squirrel, in a rage. "You, a mouse, dare to ask a grey squirrel for a favour like that! Of course I shall not get food for you! Do you think I am a servant of mice? The idea of asking such a thing!"

"I do not mean to be uncivil," said the mouse. "It is only that I have hurt my foot and cannot get food."

"Then ask someone else to do your hunting for you," said the selfish squirrel, and bounded off.

The little mouse sat at the entrance to his burrow and watched the squirrel. It was autumn, and the little grey creature was storing away tiny heaps of nuts here and there, so that when he awoke for a few warm days now and then in the winter-time he could go to his hidden stores, have a feast, and then go to sleep again.

He hid some acorns behind the ivy-bark. He put some nuts under a pile of leaves in the ditch. He scraped a little hole under the roots of the oak tree and put four nuts there. He went to the hollow tree nearby and hid seven acorns. He was well prepared for warm days in the winter!

The mouse wished he could go and take some of the nuts—but he could not move far without pain. He lay in his hole and almost starved. Then another mouse ran by, and saw the thin and hungry one.

"What's the matter?" he asked, running into the hole.

The little mouse soon told him. The other mouse listened.

"Well, you know," he said, "I would dearly love to help you, but I have a large and hungry family, and it is all I can do to find food for them. It is very scarce this year."

"I know where plenty of food is," said the little mouse eagerly. "Get it for me, and we will all share it! Look for acorns behind the ivy-bark, and in the hollow tree. Hunt under the leaves in the ditch for nuts, and under the roots of the oak tree opposite. I saw the squirrel put some there."

The other mouse ran off in glee. Sure enough, he found nuts and acorns in plenty. He carried them one by one to his own hole, fetched the first mouse, and helped him along to the hole too. Then, with all the mouse family, the first little mouse ate in peace. Soon his leg was quite well, and he could run about happily once more.

The grey squirrel slept soundly until the month of January, when there was a warm spell. He awoke and went to find his nuts—but alas for him! However hard he looked, he could *not* find anything to eat at all! His larders were empty, each one! He went back to his tree hungry, and slept again.

Then February came, and the sun sent warm fingers into the tree where the squirrel slept soundly. Once again he awoke and came scampering down, hungry as a hunter.

He searched behind the ivy-bark—no acorns there! He hunted in the ditch—no nuts there! He looked in the hollow tree—no acorns to be seen! And last of all he put his little paw in the hole he had made beneath the roots of the oak tree. No—not a nut to be found. He must go hungry.

"I shall starve!" he said, in fright. And then he suddenly caught sight of the little mouse, who was now plump and sleek. The squirrel called to him:

"Oh, Mouse, you are fat! Let me have a little of your food, I pray you! I am lean and hungry, and I cannot find any of the food I stored away. I must have looked in the wrong places."

"Last autumn I asked *you* for a little food!" said the mouse, stopping. "But you said no! Why should I help *you* now?"

"You are right," said the squirrel sadly. "I treated you badly. There is no reason why you should not treat me the same."

"Wait!" said the mouse. "There *is* a reason why I should not treat you the same, Squirrel. You and I are not alike! You are selfish and greedy, but I am not. You shall share what I have!"

He brought the squirrel two nuts and an acorn. The squirrel thanked the mouse humbly, and vowed that he would repay the mouse when he found his own stores that he had hidden away.

"I was lucky this winter," said the little mouse, with a gleam in his eye. "I found four heaps of nuts and acorns—one behind the ivy-bark—one in the ditch—one in the hollow tree—and one under the roots of the oak. So I and my friends have feasted well!"

The squirrel listened. At first he was angry, but then he remembered that after all the mouse had let him have some food.

"So these are *my* nuts and *my* acorns!" he said. "Well—I deserved to lose them for my greed! Forgive me, Mouse! Next autumn I will store up a larder for you too!"

He kept his word, and now he and the mouse are great friends, and if you see one, you will know that the other is somewhere nearby.

A PUZZLE

THE ?

I FLY in the air on my two black wings,
But none of my family ever sings!
I like the night with its starry sky—
And yet, at noon, when the sun is high
I'm out in the fields—but my wings of black
Are no longer there—and you'll hear a smack
As time and again I strike my foe!
Now what is my name? Does anyone know?

(*Answer:* Bat and Cricket-Bat.)

THE SWALLOWS

HIGH in the air the swallows fly,
Happy all the day long,
Darting about in the deep blue sky,
Singing a twittering song.

Their nests are built on the old oak beam
High in the barn so cool,
Made of clay from the little stream,
Or mud from the edge of the pool.

They play with the martins and try to race
The sickle-winged swift in flight,
And over the trees in airy grace
They fly from morning to night.

The summer is theirs, and glad and free
Through the golden days they fly,
Calling their twittering song to me
Down the windy ways of the sky.

LIGHTWING THE SWALLOW

LIGHTWING came out of a white egg in a nest made of mud. He was very tiny indeed, and at first he could see nothing in the dark barn where his mother and father had built their nest. But very soon his eyes made out the high rafters above him, and the beam on which his nest was put.

He looked at a hole in the barn roof through which he could see the blue sky. It was summer-time, so the sky was often blue. Lightwing crouched down in the nest with his brother and sister, and waited impatiently for his mother and father to come with titbits to eat.

He was a funny little thing, rather bare, with very few feathers at first. But gradually they grew, and soon Lightwing and his brother and sister were fluffy nestlings, sitting with ever-open beaks waiting for flies that their parents caught on the wing outside the big barn.

Lightwing was a swallow. He had a marvellous steel-blue back, a white vest, and a streak of chestnut-red across his chest. His legs were small and his beak was wide in its gape. His wings were long and his tail was forked prettily. He longed for the day to come when he might fly off with his father and mother.

But when the day came he was rather afraid! His brother flew out of the nest and through the door as if he had been used to flying all his short life—but Lightwing and his sister sat on the edge of the nest, trembling. Their mother suddenly flew behind them and tipped them off the nest!

Lightwing fell—but as he fell he opened his wings, and lo and behold he could fly! His wings flashed through the barn door—he was up in the air and away, rejoicing to be in the clear, sunny sky.

He learnt to catch flies on the wing with his mouth wide open. He learnt to skim the water and pick up the flies hovering over the surface. He knew that when rain was coming the flies flew lower, and he followed them. When the weather was fine the flies flew high, and Lightwing soared below the clouds, following his food there. Then people said, "The swallows fly high —it will be fine," or, "The swallows fly low—there will be rain."

Lightwing grew strong and tireless as he flew throughout the warm summer days. But one night there was a chill in the air. Lightwing was surprised. He did not like it.

"Winter is coming!" sang the robin, in his creamy

voice. "What is winter?" cried Lightwing, in his pretty twitter. "Is it something to eat?"

One night a chill north-west wind began to blow. Lightwing felt restless. He wanted to fly somewhere, but he did not know where. He wanted to go where he could no longer feel the cold wind. He flew to the barn roof to ask his friends what to do. Hundreds of swallows settled on the old red roof. They chattered and twittered restlessly. The wind blew behind them.

And then, quite suddenly, a few swallows rose up into the air and flew southwards, with the chill wind behind them. In a few moments all the waiting hundreds had risen, too, and with one accord flew to the south.

"Good-bye!" called the robin. "Good-bye till the spring!" Lightwing called good-bye and flew with the others. Over land and over sea sped the swallows, as fast as express trains, to a warmer, southern land, where the flies were plentiful and the sun was hot.

And there Lightwing is now—but when the spring comes again he will return, and maybe build his nest in your barn or mine!

GOOD AND BAD BERRIES

On the hedges the blackberries sweet
Are ready and waiting for children to eat.
The nightshade berries are ripening too,
But don't eat those, whatever you do!
And don't touch the bryony berries at all,
Or the peas in laburnum pods, shrivelled and small.
You may pick all the bilberries, ripening fast,
And knock down the hazel-nuts as you go past,
But yew-berries pink, and arum of red

Mustn't be eaten, or you'll be in bed!
Privet is bad, honeysuckle as well.
If you eat their berries, sad tales you will tell!
Mushrooms are good, so your hands you may fill,
But toadstools will certainly make you feel ill.
The golden rule is—eat the good things you *know,*
But leave all the others, wherever they grow!

MIXED-UP PROVERBS

IN each sentence there are bits of two proverbs. Find out what each is and write them out properly:

1. Make hay when the horse is gone.
2. Half a loaf is better than a bird in the bush.
3. Too many cooks make Jack a dull boy.
4. Birds of a feather shouldn't throw stones.
5. Don't cross a bridge before you leap.
6 You can take a horse all that glitters.
7. A stitch in time blows nobody any good.

BRER RABBIT'S EARTHQUAKE

ONCE, on a very hot day, Brer Rabbit sat down on a stone to rest himself. Now, this stone wasn't really a stone, it was the shell of Brer Terrapin. His head was well tucked into his shell, and he was snoozing peacefully.

But when Brer Rabbit sat down on him "Kerplonk!" he woke up in a mighty hurry. He felt Brer Rabbit's weight on his back and he could hardly breathe. So he gave himself a mighty heave and sent Brer Rabbit right off his back, rolling over and over in the dust.

Brer Rabbit was scared, and he sat up and looked round. "That must have been an earthquake!" he said. "Whiskers and tails, I'd better warn all the other creatures so's they'll be ready if it comes again."

Off he went, lippitty-clippitty through the woods, and old Brer Terrapin, he sat up and laughed till the tears ran all over his shell and made little rivers down his back.

"That's a new name for me!" he chuckled. "I'm an earthquake, am I? Oh, that's a mighty fine joke! I must go and tell Brer Fox!" So while Brer Rabbit went one way, Brer Terrapin went the other, one shivering with fear, and the other shaking with laughter.

Soon Brer Rabbit happened across Brer Wolf. "Hie, Brer Wolf!" called Brer Rabbit. "Look after yourself. I just sat on an earthquake and there might be another one along in a few minutes."

"You don't say so!" said Brer Wolf, astonished. "Well, I'll come with you and we'll go and tell Brer Bear."

Off they scampered, and soon came to where Brer Bear was licking honey out of a pot.

"Hie, Brer Bear!" said Brer Wolf. "Look after yourself. Brer Rabbit just sat on an earthquake, and he says there might be another along in a few minutes."

"Stars and moon!" said Brer Bear, scared. "You don't say so! Well, I'll come with you and we'll go and tell Brer Turkey Buzzard."

Off they went, and presently came to where Brer Turkey Buzzard was preening his long tail-feathers.

"Hie, Brer Turkey Buzzard!" called Brer Bear. "Look after yourself! Brer Rabbit just sat down on an earthquake, and he says there might be another along in a few minutes."

"Feathers and fluff!" screeched Brer Turkey Buzzard in a panic. "You don't say so! Well, I'll come with you and we'll go and tell Brer Fox."

Off they rushed and came to where Brer Fox was lying basking in the sun.

"Hie, Brer Fox!" screeched Brer Turkey Buzzard. "Look after yourself! Brer Rabbit just sat down on an earthquake, and he says there might be another along in a minute."

"Then we'd all better go and hide," said Brer Fox, shivering and shaking. "Come along. We'll get into that hollow tree. Maybe we shall be safe there."

So they all climbed into the hollow tree and lay there trembling, waiting for the next earthquake to come along.

Now old Brer Terrapin, he went along slowly to find Brer Fox to tell him the joke, and all the way he was laughing fit to kill himself.

"Brer Rabbit sits down on me, thinking I'm a stone, and when I throw him off he thinks I'm an earthquake. Oh my, oh my, who'd think Brer Rabbit was such a silly?"

Now all the crowd in the hollow tree were looking out for another earthquake, and when they saw Brer Terrapin ambling along slowly, they began to call to him to come quickly and hide with them.

"Hi, Brer Terrapin!" shouted Brer Wolf. "Come along and hide with us, quick! You'll be safe then."

Brer Terrapin looked up at the crowded tree in surprise.

"What are you all there for?" he asked.

"Oh, don't ask questions!" shouted Brer Bear. "You come along and hide before it's too late."

"But what are you hiding from?" shouted Brer Terrapin.

"An earthquake!" screeched Brer Turkey Buzzard.

"Brer Rabbit here, he just sat down on one, and he says another might be along in a minute."

Brer Terrapin stared up at them and then his big bulky body began to shake all over inside its shell.

"Ho ho ho!" he laughed. "He he he! Ha ha ha! Oh my, oh my, ho ho ho! Just listen to them! Did you ever hear the like!"

The creatures in the hollow tree thought Brer Terrapin had gone mad, and they all shouted to him loudly.

"Brer Terrapin! Come here quickly before the earthquake comes back again!"

"He he he!" wheezed old Brer Terrapin, almost dead with laughing. "I'm—I'm—*I'M* the Earthquake!"

The creatures stared at him, puzzled. "What do you mean?" shouted Brer Bear, at last. "How can a little thing like you be an earthquake? It's a most enormous great thing that shakes the earth under our feet. Are you mad, Brer Terrapin?"

"Not quite," said Brer Terrapin, wiping his eyes with his clawed hand. "Not quite. Oh, what a joke! Is Brer Rabbit there too?"

"Of course he is!" said Brer Turkey Buzzard. "He was kind enough to come and warn us all. But do come into the tree, Brer Terrapin."

"Now, you listen here," said Brer Terrapin, trying not to laugh again. "I was just sitting down under my shell snoozing in the sun when along came Brer Rabbit and sat himself down on me 'Ker-plonk!" He thought I was a stone, and to show him I wasn't I just heaved up and shot him off my back. And then he rushes off and says I'm an earthquake. Oh my, oh my, and there you all are sitting squashed up in a hollow tree because old Brer Rabbit told you I was an earthquake!"

Well, when the creatures heard that they were as

angry as could be with Brer Rabbit and they turned themselves about in the tree to find him. But he wasn't there! No, he had found a hole at the bottom and had slipped out. Ah, Brer Rabbit, you may get *into* a hole —but you can always get out of one, can't you!

OFF TO THE SOUTH

WHERE are the Cuckoos? One by one
They gathered together and then were gone.
And the Swifts that darted high and low
Cried "Summer is over and we must go!"
The Nightingale no longer sings,
South he's gone on his russet-wings,
And the Willow-wren and the Chiff-chaff, too,
Have flown to a land where the skies are blue.
The Fly-catcher's gone, for his larder's bare,
And the Blackcap's flown where there's food to spare,
The Martins are off and the Swallows sing
"Good-bye! Good-bye! We'll be back in the spring!"

We're sad when the twittering migrants go,
But they'll be back when the daffodils blow!

BLACKBERRIES

THE blackberry flowers, small and shy,
Shone in August when we passed by.

The petals fell to the ditch below,
And little green knobs began to grow.

We watched them eagerly till one day
We saw them redden on every spray.

They turned to purple, they grew and grew
And the sun shone down on them all day through.

And now they are black and juicy and sweet
Ready for children (and birds!) to eat.

So let's take our baskets and run down the lane,
For it's blackberry, blackberry time again!

A PUZZLE FOR YOU

I AM something you eat each day, perhaps at every meal; behead me and you can do this to a book; change my tail and the men in the harvest-field will do this every day; change my head and you will find me wherever there is a pile of anything; change my tail and you will find you do this when people speak to you; add a new tail and hear me beating; take away my head and my tail and find something on your head; change my tail and your teeth will do this at every meal; give me a new head and you will find me in an oven, a bonfire, or the sunshine; add yet another new head and you will find that my first is made of my last!

(*Answer:* Bread; Read; Reap; Heap; Hear; Heart; Ear; Eat; Heat; Wheat.)

GOOD-BYE, SWALLOWS!

Characters

HOUSE-SPARROW.	BLACKBIRD.
CHAFFINCH.	ROBIN.
TIT.	TWO OR MORE SWALLOWS.

BLACKBIRD. Ah! Plenty of crumbs to-day! That's good! (*Pecks them up.*) I always enjoy a good meal of crumbs—though a nice fat worm makes a fine dinner!

(CHAFFINCH *flies in.*)

CHAFFINCH. Good morning, blackbird! How are you today?

BLACKBIRD. Good morning, chaffinch! I'm well—see my glossy black wings! (*Flaps them.*)

CHAFFINCH. Winter is coming, Blackbird! I feel a chill in the air at nights.

BLACKBIRD. So do I. But I shan't mind the winter unless we get deep snow. I can nearly always find worms to eat.

(*Enter* TIT, *flying on to stage.*)

TIT. Good morning, blackbird! Good morning chaffinch! Ah! I see a coconut hanging up for me. Good! (*Goes to peck it.*)

CHAFFINCH. I can't think how you can eat that coconut! I prefer the seeds in this sunflower head. (*Pecks hard.*)

TIT. I like bones, nuts and fat! And a bit of bacon rind makes me very happy.

(*In fly* ROBIN *and* HOUSE-SPARROW.)

ROBIN. Hallo, everyone! Plenty of food about, I see!

But I am not hungry this morning—I've had some caterpillars for my breakfast.

HOUSE-SPARROW. And I've had about a hundred different things! Grubs and seeds and crumbs and fat and . . .

ROBIN. You always were a greedy little bird! You eat everything you see!

BLACKBIRD. Do you know, I believe the swallows are going to leave us soon? Isn't it a pity?

CHAFFINCH. I do like them so. They are such merry-hearted little creatures. Why are they going?

TIT. Goodness knows! *We* don't fly away in the autumn. We stay here all the winter. There is plenty to eat.

ROBIN. Let's call some of the swallows and ask them to stay with us this winter.

HOUSE-SPARROW. Good idea! The more birds the merrier! Winter is dull enough anyhow with most of the animals sleeping—if we have the twittering swallows, we shall have more fun.

BLACKBIRD. I'll call them! Swallows! Swallows! Come and talk to us for a minute!

(*Enter two or more* SWALLOWS, *flying and twittering. They cry,* "feetafeetit, feetafeetit!" *in high twittering voices. If more than two* SWALLOWS *are used, the teacher may spread the dialogue between them.*)

1ST SWALLOW. Did you call us?

BLACKBIRD. Yes, we did! We heard that you were going to fly away and leave us. Is that true?

2ND SWALLOW. Quite true! Oh yes, quite true! We couldn't stay in this cold country for the winter.

ROBIN. It isn't so cold as all that! *We* stay here and love it!

2ND SWALLOW. But there wouldn't be enough food for us. We should starve!

TIT. Nonsense! *We* don't starve! Come and share my coconut, or have a peck at my bone, swallows! These are hung up all the winter long for us.

(SWALLOWS *peck at bone and nut. Make faces of disgust.*)

1ST SWALLOW. What a horrible taste!

2ND SWALLOW. My beak would never be strong enough to eat this nut. I have a very weak beak indeed, though I can open it very wide.

CHAFFINCH. Well, if you don't like nuts or bones, never mind—you can share my seeds. I will show you where to find all kinds of wild seeds in the fields and hedgerows. I will show you where the farmyard is, and you can peck up some of the hens' corn. You may peck this sunflower head of mine too, if you like!

1ST SWALLOW (*pecking*). Oh! How horrible! What great big seeds they are! I couldn't possibly eat them!

2ND SWALLOW. Neither could I! I hate seeds. They are so hard and so horrid to eat.

CHAFFINCH (*quite offended*). Oh, very well, don't have my seeds if you don't want to!

1ST SWALLOW. Don't be cross, chaffinch. You see, our beaks are not hard and strong like yours. We cannot eat seeds at all, so they would be of no use to us as food in the winter.

BLACKBIRD. You had better share *my* food! Wouldn't you like that? I could find you great long worms.

2ND SWALLOW. No, thank you. We cannot catch anything that is on the ground—only insects that are in the air. That is why we fly all day long in the sky.

BLACKBIRD. Oh well, you can't expect worms to fly in the air! Perhaps the robin could help you?

ROBIN. No—I don't think I can. You see, my food is tiny insects and flies—and in the winter-time it is difficult for me to find enough for myself, so I have to ask my friends the children for crumbs. If they did not give me crumbs in the cold weather I think I should starve.

HOUSE-SPARROW. I can help you, swallows! We sparrows never starve. We always find plenty of food. I can take you to the hedges, to the fields, to the gardens—and all day long I can show you food of all kinds—seeds, bread, grubs—anything you like!

1ST SWALLOW. It's kind of you, sparrow—but we only like insects that fly in the air. We can only catch our food on the wing. Look—this is how we do it! We fly through the air like this—with our mouths wide open—and catch hundreds of little flies in the air—oh, thousands!

2ND SWALLOW. We fly from dawn till dusk, catching our food, and twittering, "feetafeetit, feetafeetit!" as we go.

BLACKBIRD. Well, I still don't see why you can't stay with us this winter! I find grubs and worms. The robin finds insect food too. Why can't you?

1ST SWALLOW. Blackbird, if you flew high in the air as we do, you would know that there are fewer and fewer flies up there in these cold autumn days. Soon there will be none! Fly now, all of you, and see if you can find flies.

(*All fly around—then stand still and shake their heads.*)

ROBIN. You are quite right. There are hardly any flies up in the sky now. I didn't think of that.

BLACKBIRD. Neither did I! Well—no wonder you

want to go, then! If there are no flies for you, and you cannot eat seeds, bread, nuts or find insects on the ground, you would most certainly starve. We must let you go!

1st Swallow (*shivering*). There is a very cold wind to-day! I think we must fly to-night!

Blackbird (*pointing off-stage*). Look at those telegraph wires up there! There are hundreds and hundreds of swallows gathering together on them. Are they going to fly away?

2nd Swallow. Yes, they are! We think they will go soon, and we must not be left behind. We must say good-bye, cousins!

Robin. But where are you going to?

1st Swallow. To a land far away to the south, where the sun is warm, and where the flies are many!

Chaffinch. How do you know the way?

2nd Swallow. I don't know—but we always get there all right. The wind blows behind us and helps us, you know! We go over land and sea—and at last we come to the land we want.

Tit. Come back again, won't you?

1st Swallow. Of course! We will come back to our homeland in the spring, you may be sure of that! Then the sun will be warm here, and there will be lots of food for us. We shall build our nests and be happy!

2nd Swallow. Look! The swallows are beginning to fly! We shall be left behind! Come, we must go! Good-bye, friends, goodbye!

1st Swallow. Wouldn't you like to come with us?

All. No, no!

(Swallows *fly off, after fluttering round stage once. Others wave wings in farewell.*)

Blackbird. Good-bye! good-bye! A good journey to

you, little swallows and a welcome home in the spring. Good-bye!

SWALLOWS (*off*). Good-bye, good-bye.

ALL. Good-bye! (*Bow and flutter off.*)

CURTAIN

OCTOBER

I GIVE you nuts in cloaks of green,
I give you berries, black and red,
Conkers, polished bright and clean,
Dropping down from overhead.
In the fields for you I grow
Mushrooms at the dawn of day,
And on the hedges high and low,
Old Man's beard, soft and grey.
I give you leaves of red and gold,
I bid the ivy spread its honey,
And though my nights are long and cold,
My autumn days are sweet and sunny.

BRER RABBIT AND THE APPLES

ONCE upon a time Brer Fox got up early and picked all the apples off the trees round about. When the other creatures saw this they were mighty wild. They went to Brer Fox's door and banged on it—blim-blam!

"Who's there?" shouted Brer Fox.

"We've come for our share of the apples," shouted Brer Bear.

"Well, you can have the cores when I've finished

with the apples," said Brer Fox. "Go away." The door was locked and the creatures couldn't get in. So they decided to wait for Brer Fox to come out, and then they would catch him and go in for the apples. But Brer Fox didn't come out. Brer Rabbit went and peeped in at the window, and he saw Brer Fox lying in bed with his leg all bandaged up. He ran back and told the others.

"Brer Fox is ill in bed," he said. "He's got a bad leg."

"I saw him fall out of the last apple-tree," said Brer Bear. "He must have hurt his leg then. Now what are we to do? He'll lie there and eat all those apples by himself—yes, and throw the cores at us when he's finished. I know Brer Fox and his bad manners!"

"Brer Rabbit, *you're* a mighty smart fellow," said Brer Wolf. "Can't you think of some way of getting those apples before they're all gone?"

"Maybe I can," said Brer Rabbit. "Maybe I can. Don't worry me. Just let me think!" Well, he thought for a while and then he slapped his legs and grinned. Ah, it didn't take old Brer Rabbit long to think of a way out of anything!

"I'll go and visit Brer Fox and play a little tune to him because he's ill," said Brer Rabbit. "And if I don't come out with a share of those apples, I'll eat my whiskers!"

"What are you going to do?" asked Brer Bear, astonished.

"Ah! That's *my* secret!" said Brer Rabbit. "I'd just like you to lend me your pair of blue trousers, Brer Bear, please."

"They're too big for you," said Brer Bear. But he got them out, and gave them to Brer Rabbit. Brer Rabbit put them on and skipped about gaily. My, he did look funny in Brer Bear's trousers!

"Now I want to borrow your penny whistle, Brer Mink," he said. So Brer Mink found his penny whistle and gave it to him. Brer Rabbit played a tune on it, as merry as a bee in clover.

"Now I want a jar of honey," he said. "Brer Bear, can you give me one?"

So Brer Bear, grumbling loudly, gave him a jar of thick honey. And what did Brer Rabbit do but put his paw in the jar, get it all over honey and smear it over the back of the blue trousers he was wearing! Brer Bear was angry—but the other creatures grinned. They knew Brer Rabbit was up to one of his tricks all right.

Brer Rabbit marched off to Brer Fox's, playing a gay tune on his whistle. He knocked at the door—blim-blam!

Brer Fox heard the knock at the door.

"Who's there?" he said.

"It's Brer Rabbit come to see how his old friend Brer Fox is," said Brer Rabbit.

"Poorly, Brer Rabbit," said Brer Fox, with a groan. "My leg's still bad."

"Would you like me to come in and play a little tune to you on my whistle?" asked Brer Rabbit. "You must be dull lying there."

"If you've come after my apples you can go away," said Brer Fox, who knew Brer Rabbit very well indeed. "You would fill your pockets if you got in!"

"Now look here, Brer Fox, didn't I tell you I've got my whistle with me to play you a little tune?" said Brer Rabbit. "And don't I need both hands to hold the whistle and play the tune? So how can I fill my pockets? I promise you I won't take my hands off my whistle."

"All right, you can come in, then," said Brer Fox, who was very dull and bored. "I'd like to hear a tune."

He limped across to the door and opened it, and Brer Rabbit stepped in, playing a merry tune on the whistle.

Brer Rabbit played the whistle well. He sounded like a blackbird gone mad. He danced, too, as he played, and kicked his legs up well. He didn't take his hands from his whistle, and Brer Fox laughed as he watched Brer Rabbit. At last Brer Rabbit stopped, out of breath. "I'll have to take a rest from dancing," he said. "But I can go on playing you a tune." He sat down on the heap of apples in the corner, Brer Bear's blue trousers spreading out widely over them. But Brer Rabbit didn't take his hands from his whistle—no, he knew Brer Fox was watching for that! He kept his hands on the whistle, and he played a tune so jiggy that Brer Fox longed to get up and dance.

"It's nice of you to come and cheer me up, Brer Rabbit," he said. "You can have an apple for your trouble."

"Oh, Brer Fox, I shouldn't think of it!" said Brer Rabbit at once. "I won't put a finger on your apples—I told you I wouldn't, didn't I? Now, one more tune, and I must go." He played another tune, and Brer Fox jigged up and down on the bed till the feathers flew out of the pillows. Brer Rabbit finished the tune and got up. He grinned at Brer Fox and went to the door, keeping his front towards Brer Fox and his hands on his whistle. "Good-bye, Brer Fox," he said. "I hope you'll be dancing soon!"

He went out and shut the door—and off he ran to where the other creatures were waiting for him. "Where are the apples?" they shouted.

Brer Rabbit turned himself round—and, stars and moon, there were *dozens* of apples sticking to the honey he had spread on the back of Brer Bear's wide blue trousers! He had sat down hard on them—and they had all stuck to him!

How all the creatures laughed and praised Brer Rabbit when he told them of his trick! They sat round him munching apples, and Brer Rabbit, he talked mighty biggitty that day.

And when Brer Fox saw what a lot of his apples had gone, he knew Brer Rabbit had somehow tricked him again. He got up and danced—but he danced with rage this time! Poor Brer Fox!

UNDER THE GROUND

Under the ground in a million places
Bulbs are hiding their little brown faces,
Putting out roots to hold themselves tight
Working away in the long winter night.

The snow comes down, and it softly makes
A blanket warm of its feathery flakes
On the ground it lies, and cosy and snug
The brown bulbs cuddle beneath their rug.

The sun shines out, and the melting snow
Trickles away in the earth below,
And the bulbs reach out with their roots of white
And drink up their blanket in great delight.

Soon, when the sun sends fingers warm
Down in the earth to each bulb and corm,
Little green spears will push up to see
What sort of a place the world can be!

And then all the treasure of purple and gold
Of yellow and blue that the brown bulbs hold
Is spread in the sun, and crocuses shine,
And snowdrops, scyllas and daffies are mine!

BLACKBERRY PIE

JEFFERY was cross. Just as he had planned to go blackberrying with the other children, Mother had called him to go an errand for her!

"Oh, Mother, I wanted to go and pick some blackberries with Jack and Gladys!" he grumbled. "I did want you to make me a blackberry pie to-morrow! It's too bad!"

"I'm sorry, Jeffery, but I promised Mrs. Jones she should have these books back to-day," said Mother, putting four books into a basket for Jeffery to carry. "Now don't sulk—you'll grow up ugly if you do!"

Jeffery said no more. He was fond of his mother, and he wasn't really a sulky boy. So he smiled at her and ran off—but inside he was very disappointed. It would have been so lovely to go blackberrying. There wouldn't be another chance till the next Saturday now, and it might be wet then. Bother, bother, bother!

He met Jack and Gladys with their little baskets. "Aren't you coming?" they shouted.

"I can't," said Jeffery. "I've got to go into the town to take these books to Mrs. Jones."

"Bad luck," said Jack, and he and Gladys went on their way to the fields. Jeffery began to whistle. He always found that was a very good thing to do when he felt cross. You can't feel cross if you are whistling!

He came to Mrs. Jones' house. She was at home and very glad to have the books. "It's nice of you to bring them, Jeffery," she said. "You might have been out in the fields with the others to-day, and then I wouldn't have got my books!"

"Well, I *was* going blackberrying, but Mother just called me before I went," said Jeffery.

"So you couldn't go blackberrying?" said Mrs. Jones. "What a pity! But listen, Jeffery—in my garden at the bottom a great bramble grows over the fence. I don't like blackberries, so I haven't even looked to see if there are any growing there this year. Would you like to go and see? If there are any you can pick them all!"

"Oh, thank you!" said Jeffery, pleased. He went down the garden and came to the bottom—and, sure enough, all over the fence there grew an enormous bramble! And on it were hundreds and hundreds of the biggest, ripest blackberries that Jeffery had ever seen! Not one had been picked, and they grew there in the sunshine, full of ripe sweetness.

"Good gracious!" said Jeffery, astonished and delighted. "Look at those! My goodness, I'm lucky!" He began to pick them. He ate a great many. They were the sweetest he had ever tasted! More and more he picked and more and more. His basket began to get full. His hands were wet and sticky. His mouth was purple. He was very happy indeed!

When his basket was full he went to show it to Mrs. Jones. "Splendid!" she said. "I'm so glad they will not be wasted. Ask your mother to make you a blackberry pie with them. You deserve them."

On his way home Jeffery met Jack and Gladys, and they were surprised to see his lovely big basketful. They had hardly any, for other children had been to the fields that day and picked all the ripe berries.

"Well, have some of mine!" said Jeffery, and he emptied some into their baskets. They *were* pleased! Then home he went—and his mother cried out in astonishment.

"You *have* been blackberrying after all!" How she smiled when she heard Jeffery's story—and now a big blackberry tart is baking in her oven. I'd *love* to have a slice, wouldn't you?

GUESS THESE COUNTIES!

(*Anywhere in Britain, please.*)

1. In me you will find some people.
2. And in me, too!
3. I have a stone to give you.
4. Look for a church in me.
5. In me you will find something belonging to a candle.
6. You can wear me if you like—I'll keep you warm!
7. I will give you something to lie on.
8. You'll find the head of the Royal Family in me!
9. Let me give you something to lean on.
10. In me you will find something to cross a river.

(*Answers:* The counties are—1. Norfolk (folk); 2. Suffolk (folk); 3. Flint; 4. Kirkcudbright (kirk, a church); 5. Warwick (wick); 6. Cardigan; 7. Bedford (bed); 8. Buckingham (king); 9. Stafford (staff); 10. Cambridge (bridge).

BLACKBERRY TIME

LET'S pick blackberries—it's such fun!
  I know where the best bushes are—
Come on—get your baskets, and off we'll run
  Away down the lane; it's not far!
See, here is a hedge where the blackberries grow;
  There are sprays hanging just by our heads;
The bramble-leaves, too, make a wonderful show
  In their crimsons and yellows and reds!
Look out for the prickles—they scratch like a cat!
  It's with them that the bramble-sprays climb;
See, there are some berries, black, juicy and fat,
  Oh, don't you *love* blackberry time!
Pop some in your mouth—aren't they juicy and sweet?
  We'll take hundreds home with us, too!
Blackberry puddings and tarts are a treat,
  Your mother will make some for you!

There are blackberries, blackberries all down the way,
I *wish* we could stay here the whole of the day!
Don't you?

BRER RABBIT RAISES A DUST

BRER RABBIT. BRER WOLF.
BRER FOX. BRER BEAR.
BRER TURKEY BUZZARD.

SCENE. *This is a good play for acting in the school playground. All that is needed is a good strong box covered with black felt or cloth to make it look like a rock. It should be in the middle of the stage.*

When the scene opens all the characters are sitting or standing around, talking. BRER RABBIT *is smoking a pipe and so is* BRER WOLF. BRER BEAR *is reading a newspaper.* BRER FOX *is polishing something.* BRER TURKEY BUZZARD *is walking up and down.*

BRER FOX. I'm getting tired of this polishing. It makes my arm ache.

BRER RABBIT. You always were a weak creature, Brer Fox!

BRER FOX. I don't want any of your cheek, Brer Rabbit. And don't blow your smoke in my face!

BRER RABBIT. Sorry. I didn't notice it was your face.

BRER BEAR. Be quiet, you two. Listen to what it says in this paper. It tells about a man who's so strong he can lift a piano in one hand!

BRER RABBIT. Pooh! That's nothing!

BRER TURKEY BUZZARD. Don't be silly, Brer Rabbit. Why, you couldn't even lift that rock behind you, and it must weigh much less than a piano!

BRER WOLF. Yes—you just try lifting that rock, Brer Rabbit. Then we'll see how strong you are!

BRER RABBIT (*waving pipe in air*). Lifting a rock is nothing! But *who* could kick dust out of that rock? That's what I'd like to know!

BRER FOX. Kick dust out of a rock? Well, that should be easy. I guess I could kick up a fine dust on that rock!

BRER BEAR. And I reckon I could kick up such a dust that none of you would be able to see!

BRER RABBIT. Is that so? Well, what about having a kicking match, and seeing who can kick the most dust out of this rock? Then we'll soon see who's strongest!

BRER FOX. Right! We'll each stand up on the rock and kick our hardest—and the one that kicks the most dust out is the strongest of us all—but I guess old Brer Rabbit won't win the match!

BRER TURKEY BUZZARD. We'll hold the match after

dinner. We'll all meet here again at two o'clock, and see what happens!

(*He goes out.*)

BRER BEAR. I guess my great paws can do the most damage to that rock! Yes, that's what I guess! (*Goes out.*)

BRER FOX. Come along, Brer Wolf. We'll go and have our dinner and then we'll come back and show that scamp of a rabbit what we can do.

BRER WOLF. We will! (*They go out.* BRER RABBIT *is left alone with his pipe. He sits for a moment or two in silence. Then he grins, and slaps his knee. He gets up and looks at the rock.*)

BRER RABBIT. Well, well, I don't somehow think any of us will knock much dust out of that hard old rock —but I'm going to all right! Yes, I am—and I know how I'm going to do it too!

(*He takes off his shoes, which are very big. Bedroom slippers are the best to wear, to get the most effect.*)

BRER RABBIT. Now, where are some ashes? If I fill my slippers with those, I guess I'll raise a bit of dust when it's my turn to get up on that rock!

(*He goes round to back of rock, and brings out a tin or pan of fine grey ashes. He empties some into each slipper, grinning and chuckling to himself all the time.*)

BRER RABBIT. My, this is going to be fun! Won't the others stare! They won't know the dust is in my shoes, not out of the rock. Oh, I'm a smart fellow I am, a real scamp of a rabbit!

(*He replaces tin behind rock, and then puts on*

the slippers very carefully indeed. He blows away any ash left on the ground. Then he sits down against the rock and pretends to light his pipe again. He shuts his eyes and sleeps.)

VOICES (*off-stage*). Come along, it's time!
Hurry up, Brer Wolf!
Who's going to raise the biggest dust?

(*Enter* BRER WOLF, BRER FOX, BRER TURKEY BUZZARD *and* BRER BEAR.)

BRER WOLF. There's Brer Rabbit come back first! Heyo, Brer Rabbit! Wake up!

BRER RABBIT (*awaking*). Heyo, Brer Wolf! Heyo, everybody!

BRER FOX. Here we all are back again. Get up, Brer Rabbit, and let the match begin. You try first.

BRER RABBIT (*getting up carefully so as not to let ash fly out of his slippers*). Oh no—I'm the smallest. You big ones must go first.

BRER BEAR. Well then, I guess I'll try first. Watch me kick the dust out of this rock, brothers!

(*He gets up on to the rock. He begins to do a sort of shuffling dance, kicking the rock with his heels.*)

BRER FOX (*bending down to look*). Not a speck of dust, Brer Bear. No use at all!

BRER BEAR (*puzzled*). Well, and I'm such a big fellow too! (*He gets down.* BRER FOX *gets up.*)

BRER FOX (*grinning*). Watch me, brothers! I guess you'll see the dust fly now! (*Kicks and stamps hard. Everyone watches for dust.*)

BRER TURKEY BUZZARD. No good, Brer Fox. Your feet aren't strong enough to kick dust out of that old rock. Let *me* try! (*He climbs up and* BRER FOX *jumps down.*)

BREER WOLF. Go it, Brer Turkey Buzzard! Kick hard! Let's see the dust fly! (BRER TURKEY BUZZARD *does his best and several times nearly falls off the rock.*)

BRER RABBIT. Poor, Brer Turkey Buzzard, poor! Not a speck of dust to be seen. You are none of you as strong as I am!

BRER WOLF. Ho, *you*! A feeble creature like you won't raise much dust, that's certain! Get down, Brer Turkey Buzzard. It's my turn. Get your hankies out, all of you, for I'll just about choke you with my dust!

(*Gets up and begins to pound on the rock with his feet. Everyone watches.*)

BRER TURKEY BUZZARD. Go on, Brer Wolf! There's no dust yet!

BRER FOX. A poor show, Brer Wolf, a poor show!

BRER RABBIT. Who would have thought he was such a weak fellow?

BRER WOLF (*angrily*). Don't you talk to me like that, Brer Rabbit. Just *you* come along up here and see what *you* can do! If you raise any dust I'll eat my hat!

(BRER WOLF *jumps down and* BRER RABBIT *gets up carefully. He stands grinning on the rock. He puts his hands in his pockets and shouts out gaily.*)

BRER RABBIT. Now, folks, look out! You want to see dust kicked out of this rock by the strongest fellow in the world? All right then—here goes!

(BRER RABBIT *begins to shuffle and dance and stamp, and the ash flies out of his slippers, looking as if he were kicking dust out of the rock. Everyone is astonished.*)

BRER FOX. Look at that! He's kicking the dust out!

BRER WOLF. Where's my handkerchief? I'm choking!

BRER BEAR. He must be mighty strong to do that! A-tish-oo! A-tish-oo!

BRER TURKEY BUZZARD. Stop it, Brer Rabbit! We're all coughing and sneezing with the dust.

BRER RABBIT (*going on with his dance on the rock*). Well, do you think I'm the strongest of you all? Do you think I can raise more dust out of this rock than you can?

ALL. Yes, yes, Brer Rabbit!

BRER FOX. You're a mighty strong man!

BRER BEAR. You come along down now, Brer Rabbit, before we're all choked!

(BRER RABBIT *grins, gives a last stamp with both feet and jumps down.*)

BRER RABBIT. Well, folks, I'm glad you think I've won. What's the prize?

BRER FOX. Nothing! We didn't say a word about a prize.

BRER RABBIT (*threateningly*). What! No prize for a strong fellow like me!

BRER FOX (*scared*). Well—since you're so mighty strong—maybe we'd better give him a prize, folks?

ALL. Yes, give him a prize.

BRER RABBIT. I'll have a carrot from you, Brer Wolf, a lettuce from you, Brer Fox, an onion from you, Brer Turkey Buzzard, and a potato from you, Brer Bear.

BRER WOLF. Now that's not fair to ask for all those prizes!

BRER RABBIT. What! You dare to refuse me that! I'll fight you! (*Puts up his fists.* BRER WOLF *steps back in alarm. Everyone looks frightened.*)

BRER BEAR. Now now, Brer Rabbit, we don't want to fight a great strong fellow like you, who can kick dust out of a rock. We'll go and get the prizes for you.

BRER RABBIT (*stamping his foot*). Well *go* then!

(*They all rush off in a panic, tripping and stumbling.*)

BRER RABBIT (*sitting on rock, crossing his legs and looking very pompous*). Ho! They're all afraid of *me,* the strongest rabbit in the world!

CURTAIN

WHAT AM I?

I may grow in your garden
In a tidy little hedge,
Or you *may* use me for flowers
Upon your window ledge.
Perhaps I keep your matches,
And your pencils, too—how queer
But oh, I hope you never
Will feel me on your ear!

(*Answer:* Box.)

THE SEED TRAVELLERS

ONCE there was a little girl called Eileen. She had been for a walk in the country, and she was so tired that now she sat down beneath a bush and had a rest. And as she sat there, her eyes shut, enjoying the wind on her cheek, she heard the plants around her talking.

First the big thistle nearby spoke, in a scratchy sort of voice.

"It's time to send my seeds away! I would like to send them to that field over there. There are no thistles there. There would be plenty of room for them to grow. I shall ask the wind to help me."

Eileen opened her eyes and saw the wind puff at the thistle. At once a little cloud of thistledown blew away. It floated bit by bit to the distant field, and there each downy seed rested, ready to grow into new thistle plants the following year.

"The wind is a good friend to you, thistle!" said the voice of a nearby gorse-bush. "But I prefer to let the sun help *me*! I ask it to shine hotly down on my pods and dry them up. Then they twist up and as they twist they shoot out my hard brown seeds like this!"

There came a sharp popping noise, and something hit Eileen on the cheek! It was the seeds of the gorse-bush behind her! She turned to look at it. Sure enough it was full of twisted black pods—the seeds had been shot out like little bullets! Some had even gone into the next field!

"What funny ways the plants have of sending their seeds on their travels!" thought Eileen, rubbing her cheek. "I didn't know they were so clever."

Another voice spoke. It was the wild rose-bush just behind. It had a gentle voice. "My seeds, too, must be sent away for next year's growing," it said. "But I do not use the wind or the sun. I get the birds to help me. Watch this thrush! See how he scatters my seeds for me!"

A big freckled thrush flew down to the bush and pecked at a ripe scarlet hip. He flew off to a gate near-by with it. He pecked at the juicy scarlet covering, but the hard, hairy seeds inside, which he did not like, he dropped to the ground.

"Did you see that?" said the rose-bush, pleased. "That thrush has dropped six seeds for me. They will all grow into new rose-shoots in the spring! Good! My seeds will do well! It is a fine idea to grow a bright juicy covering to seeds, for then birds will come to eat it, and will cast away the hard seeds inside."

A tiny voice spoke from just beside Eileen. "You all have very good ideas," said the little voice, and Eileen saw that it came from a clump of goose-grass. "Some of you use the wind, like the thistle and the dandelion, the ash and the sycamore. Some use the sun, like the gorse and the little violet. Some use birds, like the rose and the hawthorn—but I am cleverer than any of you. *I* am going to make this little girl plant my seeds!"

"You are not!" cried Eileen, and she jumped up. "It's time for me to go home!"

She ran off—but she did not see that she had some tiny rounded seeds sticking to her woollen stockings! They were the seeds of the goose-grass! They were covered with tiny hooks that clung tightly to the wool. Eileen brushed them away when she felt them clinging there.

And they fell to the ground at the bottom of the hill—and there they grew into new goose-grass plants. But Eileen didn't know. Wasn't the goose-grass clever!

THE LAST FEAST OF AUTUMN

On my wall the ivy grows,
And now, when other flowers are dead,
A thousand buds of green it shows,
And soon a honeyed feast is spread
For starving flies and drowsy bees,
For hungry wasps and beetles bright,
Who dip as often as they please
Into the nectar with delight.
The peacock butterflies are there,
Red Admirals spread their gaudy wings,
And blustering blue bottles share
The feast that ivy blossom brings.

Drink and be glad, you creatures small,
For soon Jack Frost, with fingers white,
Will creep along the ivied wall,
And nip you cruelly in the night!

THE LOVELY PRESENT

THE Little Princess Peronel had been ill. The King and Queen were glad when she began to get better, and they hoped very much she would soon be happy and bright again. It was dreadful to see her looking so sad.

In the middle of November the Princess had her birthday. It would soon arrive, and the King meant to make it a very grand affair.

"Perhaps the Princess will cheer up when she sees all her presents arriving!" he thought. "I will send out a notice to say that everyone must try to think of something really good this year."

As soon as the people knew that the King hoped for plenty of amusing presents for Peronel, they set to work to make them, for they all loved the little girl. One carved a big wooden bear for her that could open its mouth and growl. One made a whistle from an elder twig that could carol like a bird. There were any amount of lovely presents!

There was one small boy who badly wanted to give the Princess something, but he couldn't think what. He had no money. He couldn't carve a toy. He couldn't even make a whistle. He really didn't know *what* to do.

And then one day he did a very queer thing. It was a windy morning and the last leaves were blowing down from the trees. The little boy went out with a small sack. He stood under the trees, and every time the wind blew down a gust of dry leaves he tried to catch one. All that day he worked and all the next. In fact, he worked for nine days without stopping, and by that time his sack was quite full!

Then, on the birthday morning, he set out to the palace with the sack of leaves on his back. Everyone wondered what he had! Hundreds of other people were on the way, too, all with toys and presents. But alas for the King's hopes! Not one of the presents made the sad little Princess even smile.

Towards the last of all came the small boy with his sack. "What have you got there?" asked the King, in surprise. "A year of happy days for the little Princess!" said the boy. He opened his sack and emptied all the dry, rustling leaves over the surprised Princess. Everyone stared in astonishment.

"Don't you know that for every leaf you catch in autumn before it touches the ground you will have a happy day next year?" said the little boy to the Princess. "Well, I have caught three hundred and sixty-five for you, so that's a whole year. They're for you, because I'd like you to be happy and well again—so here they all are! And, as this is the first day of your new birthday year, you must smile and be happy!"

And she did, because she was so pleased. Wasn't it a good idea? Have *you* caught any happy days this autumn?

WHO—WHO—WHO?

THE squirrel woke up on a sunshiny day
And he scrambled out of his hole to play,
He looked for the nuts he had hidden away,
But he couldn't find one,
Not one!
"Now who has taken my nuts?" he cried,
"They were here in this cranny, well tucked inside,
They took me a week and a half to hide,
But now there are none,
There are none!"
He told the owl, and that night she flew
Under the stars twinkling frosty-blue,
Calling excitedly, "Who-who-who
Is the wicked thief?
The thief!"
A plump little mouse heard the hooting call
As he crouched in his hole 'neath the mossgrown wall,
And he grinned to himself, but said nothing at all,
But it's *my* belief
He's the thief!

THE SQUIRRELS AND THE NUTS

THERE were once two red squirrels who lived in Windy Woods.

When the autumn came and nuts hung on the hazel-trees the two feasted merrily. They went to the beech-trees, too, and picked out the kernels of the beech nuts. What a fine time they had!

Then a cold, bitter wind began to blow through Windy Woods, and although the squirrels wrapped themselves up well in their bushy tails, they could not keep themselves warm.

"Let us go to our nests and sleep whilst the cold weather lasts," said one squirrel.

"First we must hide some nuts," said the other. "We shall be hungry when we wake up."

So one squirrel hid his nuts in the crack of a tree, and the other hid his under a pile of dead leaves. Then they each went to their nest, curled themselves up and fell fast asleep.

Now when February came, the sun shone out warmly for two or three days, and the primroses began to peep in Windy Woods. The two squirrels woke up and stretched themselves. Cold weather might come again—but they were not going to sleep through this warm spell! No—they wanted a game and a meal! Out they frisked and said good morning to one another. Then they began to hunt for their nuts. They soon found them, just where they had hidden them—in the crack of a tree, and under the pile of dead leaves in the ditch. But then they began to quarrel about whose nuts were which.

"I tell you *I* put my nuts in this tree!" chattered one squirrel, "and *you* put your nuts under the leaves! Mine are bigger and better than yours!"

"You storyteller!" cried the second squirrel. "I

know quite well that the nuts in the ditch are yours—all the rest are mine! You are greedy—you want the best, that's what it is!"

"Take that!" cried the first squirrel, in anger, and struck the other a blow on the nose. Then they began to fight, crying, "The nuts in the tree are mine! The ones in the ditch are yours!"

They made such a noise that two wood-mice, a dormouse and a nuthatch bird came to see what was the matter. A hedgehog came too—but after a few minutes only the hedgehog was to be seen watching. The others had gone. The squirrels fought till they had no breath left, and had pulled out a great deal of their pretty coats. Then they sat and panted.

"Let us *share* all the nuts," said the first one. "Then we shall each have the same."

So they ran to get the nuts—but to their great surprise, not a single one was there! None was in the tree or in the ditch either! Not one!

"Have *you* taken them?" they shouted to the watching hedgehog.

"I!" said the hedgehog in scorn, "I never eat nuts! I like beetles and grubs. Ask the two wood-mice, the dormouse and the nuthatch bird, not me! People who lose their tempers lose other things too!"

Off he went—and in their homes the two wood-mice and the dormouse chuckled as they gnawed at the nuts—and the nuthatch laughed too, as he wedged a hazel nut into the bark of a tree and split open the shell with his hard beak. Only the two squirrels didn't laugh. They looked at one another and nodded their pretty heads. "Yes, yes," they said sorrowfully, "it's true—people who lose their tempers lose other things too!"

THE SLEEPY SNAIL

THE snail looked out on a frosty day,
"It is time," he said, "that I hid away."
So he went with his house to an ivied wall,
And found a hiding-place, dark and small.
Said the sleepy snail, "My house I will close,
And then, safe and sound, I will happily doze;"
So inside he went, and before the night fell
He grew a stout door for the hole in his shell!
So no one can creep in his round little house,
He's safe from a bird, a beetle, or mouse!
Behind his front door, so horny and strong,
The sleepy snail dozes the whole winter long!

(If you find a snail this winter, look at the fine front door he has grown.)

COLD WEATHER

THE sky is grey, the wind is cold,
The hungry birds are tame and bold,
There's ice beside the running river
Where the wagtails stand and shiver.
Frost climbs up each blade of grass,
And every puddle shines like glass;
The lane is powdered white with snow
And carefully the horses go
For fear they slip; within the fold
The little lambs are safe from cold,
And when we breathe, our breath comes out
Like steam from any kettle-spout!

THE LITTLE BEGGARS

SITTING in a row were ten little beggars. They were cold, hungry and miserable. Five were dressed in brown, one had a red waistcoat, one a pink vest, one a glossy black coat, one had freckles, and the last had a black cap. Who were they? Well, my dears, they were five brown sparrows, one robin redbreast, one pink-chested cock chaffinch, one blackbird, one thrush, and one great tit!

They sat on the fence of the school garden and shivered. The ground was frozen hard. They could find no worms, no insects, no seeds, no fruit. They could not even find water to drink, for the pond they usually drank from was frozen.

Miss Brown, the teacher, looked out of the window and saw them. She saw the robin fluff out his red chest to keep himself warm. She saw the sparrows crouch down on their feet, which were as cold as ice. She saw the blackbird peck at some snow to see if he could get a drink out of it—but, of course, he couldn't.

Miss Brown had a kind heart. "Just look!" she said to the children. "Ten little beggars are begging us to help them! What shall we do?"

The children had kind hearts, too. They all crowded round the window and stared at the ten little beggars.

"I shall make a bird-table," said Peter, the biggest boy. "I know how to. It's just a pole stuck in the ground with a flat piece of wood at the top."

"And I have an old enamel dish at home," said Mary, the head-girl. "I shall bring it and keep it filled with water for the birds to drink."

"And I shall bring a coco-nut," said Eileen. "My father is a greengrocer, and he will give me one if I ask him."

"I shall bring a little pot of dripping," said Tom. "My mother bakes to-day and she is sure to have a little over. The tits will like that."

"I shall bring all the scraps my mother can spare," said the smallest boy. "I've got an empty cream carton at home that I play with. I shall fill it each morning with scraps and empty it on the table that Peter's going to make."

"I shall do that, too," said Polly. "And I will ask mother if I can bring a potato to school baked in its skin. It will keep my hands warm all the way to school, and then the birds can eat it on the table. Don't you think that's a good idea, Miss Brown?"

"Yes, if your mother can spare the potato," said Miss Brown. "A very good idea! *I* am going to buy some pea-nuts this very day, and this afternoon we will all help to thread them on string. We will make a big, big necklace of them, and hang it in loops all the way round Peter's table—then we shall have the fun of seeing the tits swing on them to peck out the brown kernels inside."

"I shall bring one of my dog's bones," said Joyce. "We'll hang it up. Perhaps the starlings will like it, as well as the tits."

That was last week, children! Yesterday I went by the school, and, dear me! do you suppose there were ten little beggars there, sitting on the school fence? No, there were not—but I counted fourteen sparrows, two robins, six starlings, three blackbirds, two thrushes, two chaffinches, and four tits in the school garden, all having a fine time on or near the table that Peter had made!

Have you ten little beggars too? Look out of the window and see. You'll know what to do with them if you have!

GUESS!

THE fourth of April please to find,
And then November the third,
Now in July look behind——
Then write down a word
That spells a plant whose blossoms green
On wall and hedge can now be seen!

(*Answer:* Ivy.)

JACK FROST

EVERY little twig of brown
He lightly powders up and down,
Every blade of grass is bright
With tiny crystals, dazzling white;
On the spider threads he grows
Frosty beads in shining rows,
Changing into fairy lace
All the webs in every place!
He sits upon our window-sill
And paints with rare and loving
skill
Leaf and frond in rich design
On your window-pane and mine.
Silently he comes and goes,
Unseen as the wind that blows.
Leaving loveliness behind
For our eyes to seek and find.

THE FIR TREE

FIR tree, fir tree, straight and tall,
I wonder what you will be!
What do you wish for most of all?
Whisper your dreams to me!
Would you be the mast of a beautiful yacht,
And sail on the river blue,
Or a telegraph pole in a busy spot,
Humming the whole day through?
Or say, would you rather come home with me
One snowy, Christmassy day,
And change in a trice to a Christmas tree,
Shining and lovely and gay?

THE CHRISTMAS TREE

NOTE

THIS play is an unusual one, as it brings in the audience too. It is good for a Christmas party. The presents can be such little things as pencils, notebooks, and so on.

The *real* names of the children must be called out, of course, and real abilities or characteristics commented on. This makes it all very real and very funny. I, of course, have used made-up names and remarks.

Characters

FATHER CHRISTMAS.

ELSIE BROWN JIMMY BROWN FREDDIE BROWN	three children.	JINGLE PIP TIPPY	his servants.

SCENE. *An ordinary room in the Browns' house. One or two chairs or stools are about. There is a table at the back. When the play opens,* ELSIE *and* JIMMY *are sitting on chairs or stools, and* JIMMY *is reading aloud, whilst* ELSIE *knits.*

JIMMY. And then they lighted up the Christmas tree, and it shone like magic. At the top was a fairy doll, and all around its branches hung the most exciting presents. . . . I say, Elsie, I do wish *we* had a Christmas tree, don't you?

ELSIE. Yes, I do! But we've never had one yet, and I don't suppose we ever will. Anyway, we'd never get any presents to hang on it—they cost such a lot of money!

(*A noise is heard off-stage. Somebody is singing a song, and walking heavily.*)

JIMMY. There's Freddie! I'd know his big feet anywhere! Hie, Freddie, come along in out of the cold!

(*Enter* FREDDIE—*and over his shoulder is a Christmas tree. He grins at the others.*)

FREDDIE. Hallo! Look what I've got! Mr. Jones gave it to me because I swept the snow away from his path this morning! It's a Christmas tree! (*Shows it.*)

ELSIE. It's lovely! We were just saying that we'd never had one—and now we have!

JIMMY. It's not much use, though. A Christmas tree is only a fir-tree when it's not decorated. It isn't a Christmas tree till it's hung with toys and things!

FREDDIE. Elsie, get that old tub. We'll pop it in that, and stand it on the table.

ELSIE (*running out*). All right!

JIMMY. Wouldn't it be lovely if the tree was full of presents, Freddie? It would look beautiful then.

(*Enter* ELSIE *with tub. The boys put the tree inside, and use either earth or sand to keep it steady.*)

FREDDIE. In you go, little tree. Spread out your roots. Stand steady now!

ELSIE (*laughing*). You talk to it as if it were a horse, Freddie!

JIMMY (*standing back*). There! It looks fine!

ELSIE. Freddie! Jimmy! Do let's wish a wish! Let's wish for our tree to be a *real* Christmas tree, and have presents on it!

JIMMY. Don't be silly, Elsie!

FREDDIE. Oh, well, she's only a girl! Let her wish if she wants to. Wishes never come true! Go on, wish then, Elsie!

ELSIE (*standing in front of stage, shutting her eyes tightly, screwing up her nose, and clasping her hands together over her chest in excitement*). I wish—I wish—I wish——

BOYS. Go *on*, Elsie!

ELSIE. I wish that our tree was a real Christmas tree with presents hanging all round it! (*She opens her eyes and blinks.*)

FREDDIE. Well—look at the tree, Elsie! Your wish didn't come true!

(*They all look sadly at the empty tree. As they stand there, the noise of jingling bells is heard, faint at first, and then more and more loudly. Then the sound of galloping hoofs is heard as well. The children listen.*)

ELSIE. Listen! What's that noise of bells? It's like sleigh-bells!

JIMMY. And that sound of hoofs galloping over the snow—it's like . . . Oh, listen!

(*Bells again. Then a loud voice shouting "Whoa there! Whoa! Steady, I say!" Bells jingle again faintly. Noise of footsteps heard. Enter* FATHER CHRISTMAS.)

FATHER CHRISTMAS (*in a breezy, rollicking voice*). Hallo, hallo! Don't look so scared! Did somebody wish a Christmas-tree wish just now?

ELSIE. Yes—yes! *I* did! Oh, are you really Father Christmas?

FATHER CHRISTMAS. Well, I don't look like Mickey Mouse, do I? Of course I'm Father Christmas. And I've come to grant your wish. What was it you wanted!

JIMMY. Elsie wanted our little Christmas tree to be full of presents, sir! Can you really grant her wish?

FATHER CHRISTMAS. Of course! Just wait a minute till I get my servants here! Hie, Jingle! Hie, Pip! Where are you, Tippy?

(*Enter three or more servants. They bow to the children, who look most astonished.*)

JINGLE. You called us, Father Christmas?

FATHER CHRISTMAS. Yes. I want you to go and get some toys out of my sack to hang on this tree. Hurry! Bring in the sack.

PIP. Very good sir! (*They hurry out, and re-enter at once dragging a heavy sack.*)

FREDDIE. I say! Is that the sack of toys you take round with you on Christmas night, Father Christmas?

FATHER CHRISTMAS. Yes, my boy—and I've got hundreds more sacks as well! Now then, my lads—fill up that Christmas tree quickly!

SERVANTS. Yes, sir; we'll hurry!

(FATHER CHRISTMAS *puts his hand into sack and draws out many small toys, which he gives to the servants. Each toy is supplied with a loop of string so that it can be easily hung on the tree.*)

FATHER CHRISTMAS. Here's a book! Take it, Jingle! Here's a train! And here are some tiny dolls!

FREDDIE (*peeping inside sack*). Are there any boats, Father Christmas? I would so like one!

FATHER CHRISTMAS (*bringing out some tiny boats*). Yes—there is everything in here! It doesn't matter what toy you ask for, it'll come out of this sack!

ELSIE. A ball, please, Father Christmas! (*A ball is brought out.*)

FREDDIE. A book! (*A book comes out.*)

JIMMY. A pencil! (*Out come two or three at once. The servants take each thing and hang it quickly some-*

where on the tree. Soon it is full, and looks very pretty.)

ELSIE (*admiring the tree*). It looks lovely now—but, oh, Father Christmas, there are *far* too many toys for *us*! We couldn't possibly have all those for ourselves!

FATHER CHRISTMAS. Well, give a party then, and let other children share the tree.

JIMMY. We can't—there aren't any children living near us at all.

(FATHER CHRISTMAS *rubs his head and thinks. He stares out over the audience, and then pretends suddenly to catch sight of them.*)

FATHER CHRISTMAS (*pointing to audience*). Look! Look at all those children there! What about *them*? Can't we give a party for *them*?

FREDDIE. Of course! What a lot of children! However did they get there?

JIMMY (*looking at audience in pretended amazement*). Well! Fancy that! They must have known we had a Christmas tree to-day!

JINGLE. Please, Father Christmas, sir, you ought to hurry. You've a long way to go this evening.

FATHER CHRISTMAS (*bustling to tree*). So I have; so I have! Well, I'd better get out my note-book and see if I've the names of any of those children down in it. If they've been good, they shall certainly have a present. (*He opens a giant note-book and turns over pages quickly.*) Ah! Here we are! Ellen Jackson! Has been good all the year! Is she here? (ELLEN *answers from the audience.* FREDDIE *takes a present from the tree and gives it to one of the servants who runs to* ELLEN *to give her the toy.*)

FATHER CHRISTMAS. Harry White! Has worked hard all term! Here's a fine pencil for him, Jimmy!

(JIMMY *takes the pencil from the tree and hands it to a servant, who runs to* HARRY.) Joan Townsend! She has helped her mother very well, I know. Get her a doll, Elsie. (ELSIE *does so.*) Jack Daniels! I've heard that he is very good at sums. Give him a notebook, Freddie.

JIMMY. Go on, Father Christmas! See if you have everyone's name down! I hope you've got ours too!

FATHER CHRISTMAS. Freddie Brown! Works very hard to help everyone! Choose what you'd like, Freddie!

(FREDDIE *chooses himself a boat, and shows it proudly to the audience.*)

FATHER CHRISTMAS. Elsie Brown! Now what have I got written here about you? Never makes a fuss about going to bed at night! Good girl! Choose your present!

ELSIE. Oh, thank you! (*Chooses a ball.*)

FATHER CHRISTMAS. And now it's Jimmy's turn. Jimmy Brown! Never cries when he's hurt! Good boy, Jimmy! Choose your present!

JIMMY. A book, please! (JINGLE *hands him one off the tree.*)

ELSIE. There's some more children who haven't got presents, Father Christmas. Look—there's Violet, and George, and John, and Peter and . . .

FATHER CHRISTMAS. Wait a minute! Wait a minute! Let's see if I've got them all down as good children. Violet—George—yes, give them toys, servants. John—Peter—Queenie—dear me, what a lot!

(*As the names are read the servants dart to and fro, handing the audience the little gifts.* FREDDIE, JIMMY *and* ELSIE *hand them to the servants from the tree.*)

JIMMY. Now *everyone*'s got presents, Father Christmas, and the tree is almost empty. Thank you ever so much!

FATHER CHRISTMAS. It's a pleasure, a most unexpected pleasure! Now, where's my sack? I must really go! I can hear my reindeer getting *most* impatient outside! (*Picks up sack.*) Good-bye, children! See you on Christmas Eve! But mind you're asleep and don't see *me*! (*Goes out, waving his hand to audience.*)

THREE CHILDREN. Good-bye! Good-bye! (*Servants bow and run out too. The children stare after them.*)

FREDDIE. There he goes! Hark at the bells!

(*Jingling of bells and galloping of hoofs again heard. Sound of voices shouting "Gee-up, then, gee-up!" Bells get fainter and fainter and then stop altogether.*)

FREDDIE (*his face beaming, as he addresses audience*). Well, WASN'T that a fine surprise, children?

CURTAIN

CHRISTMAS CAROL

"WE saw Him there," the oxen said,
"He had our manger for His bed."

I perched upon a beam above;
He heard me cooing," said the dove.

The donkey brayed, "So warm He lay
Because I gave Him all my hay."

"We came to have a little peep,"
The hen said, "but He was asleep."

I wish that we, too, could have crept
To kiss Him gently as He slept.

BRER RABBIT IS SANTA CLAUS!

ONCE Brer Fox got into Brer Rabbit's carrot-patch and dug up a whole sackful of his best carrots. Brer Rabbit was away visiting Brer Bear, and he didn't know anything about it till he got home. Then he was mighty angry when he saw his carrot-patch all dug up and his best carrots gone!

"Brer Fox has been here!" said Brer Rabbit. "Yes, there's the mark of his paws, and there's where his tail brushed the earth. I'll go along and make him give up my carrots or my name's not Brer Rabbit."

Well, he went along; but Brer Fox wasn't going to give up those carrots! No, he was going to have carrot soup right along till the New Year, and he wouldn't so much as open the door to Brer Rabbit!

"You go away, Brer Rabbit!" he said. "There's many a time you've taken things from me, so you can't grumble if I've taken something from you. I shan't be out of my house till the New Year, and I shall keep my door bolted and my window shut! Your carrots are as good as eaten already!"

Well, Brer Rabbit kicked at the door, blim-blam, and he hammered at the door, rickity-rack, but it wasn't a bit of good. And presently old Brer Rabbit went off in a great rage. But soon he began to do a little dance, and by the time he got home he was in a mighty good temper. Brer Rabbit had a plan in his head, and he was going to get back his carrots all right!

On Christmas Eve, with a sackful of stones on his shoulder, he climbed up on to Brer Fox's roof. He scrabbled about in the chimney, and Brer Fox heard him. "Who's up there?" yelled Brer Fox. "Go away! I'm having my supper!"

"It's Santa Claus," said Brer Rabbit, in a deep

voice. "I've got a sack of presents for you, Brer Fox."

"Come on down, then," said Brer Fox, pleased.

"I can't," said Brer Rabbit. "I'm stuck." Brer Fox unbolted his door and went into the garden to look up at the roof. Sure enough, in the moonlight, he could see someone in his chimney. He went back indoors and shouted up.

"Well, Santa Claus, never mind about coming down yourself. Just push down the sack of presents and I'll get hold of it."

"That's stuck, too," said Brer Rabbit. "You'll have to climb up the chimney a bit yourself, Brer Fox, and catch hold of the string of the sack to pull it down."

"Easy enough!" cried Brer Fox, and up the chimney he went. In a trice Brer Rabbit slipped off the roof and in at the open door. There was the sack of carrots in a corner. He whipped it up, and then he saw on the table a fine cooked goose and a great plum pudding. He rammed those down into the sack, too, then off he went through the snowy garden, chuckling like a dozen hens clucking!

Old Brer Fox climbed higher and higher up the chimney and felt about for the sack. He found the string which was hanging down. He pulled it, and it opened the neck of the sack. Out tumbled all the stones, clitter-clatter, ran-dan-dan, down the chimney, on top of Brer Fox's head. My, he went down a lot more quickly than he went up!

Poor Brer Fox! It would have been cheaper for him to have given Brer Rabbit the carrots when he asked for them, for now he has lost his goose and his pudding, too!

THE LITTLE KING

ONCE was born a mighty King,
The Lord of Heaven and Earth,
And yet for Him no bells did ring,
No shouts proclaimed His birth;
No carven cradle waited Him,
No fair and fleecy shawl,
His nursery was a stable dim,
His cot a manger small;
His blankets were the oxen's hay,
His nurse His own dear Mother;
Thus was He born on Christmas Day,
The little King, our Brother.

Coming in Armada

December 1971

ANIMAL GHOSTS

Edited by Carolyn Lloyd

Price 20p